D1070996

The Library of Scandinavian Literature

VÍGA-GLÚM'S SAGA

AND

THE STORY OF ÖGMUND DYTT

VÍGA-GLÚM'S SAGA

and

THE STORY
OF ÖGMUND DYTT

TRANSLATED FROM THE OLD ICELANDIC
WITH INTRODUCTIONS BY LEE M. HOLLANDER

LIBRARY OF SCANDINAVIAN LITERATURE

TWAYNE PUBLISHERS, INC., NEW YORK
&
THE AMERICAN-SCANDINAVIAN FOUNDATION

The Library of Scandinavian Literature

Erik J. Friis, *General Editor*

Volume 14

Víga-Glúm's Saga and The Story of Ögmund Dytt

Copyright © 1972, Twayne Publishers, Inc.

Library of Congress catalogue card number: 77-186718

MANUFACTURED IN THE UNITED STATES OF AMERICA

Contents

VÍGA-GLÚM'S SAGA

Introduction

It is understandable why *Víga-Glúm's Saga* has not at-
tracted translators:[1] unquestionably inferior in depth and
emotional appeal to the best of the Sagas of Icelanders,
such as *Egil's Saga, Laxdœla Saga, Njál's Saga,* and *Hrafn-
kel's Saga,* its style also lacks the elegance and incisive-
ness of the best Icelandic prose. Its narrative often is
halting and patchy, and there is comparatively little to
mitigate the monotony of constant fighting and feuding,
alternating with acrimonious litigation. Few sagas are
so devoid of eroticism in any sense.

Essentially, our saga is the biography of the hero whose
name it bears. He is the only outstanding one of the
numerous chieftains of the districts surrounding the Eyjafjörð, domineering, litigious, vengeful, unscrupulous, and
cunning—an anti-hero if you please. Yet he has redeem-
ing qualities. He is a leader, resolute and resourceful, a
brave fighter but also ready to lend a helping hand when
needed, as even his enemies concede, one evidently able
to inspire the loyalty and fidelity, not only of his kinsmen, but also of underlings; witness the fact that two of

his thralls are ready to sacrifice their lives in battle, shielding their fallen master with their bodies.

Far less distinctly we see the more or less stereotyped figures of his friends and enemies, barring, perhaps the shrewd but irresolute Thórarin, the overly cautious Einar Eyjólfsson, the troublemaker Thorvarð, characterized with the typical understatement as "not altogether well-intentioned," the man who tries to be friends with both parties, but is caught between the upper and lower mill stones, risking the life and future of the youth Guðmund. Among the women we may remember Glúm's long-suffering mother, Ástríð, his kind-hearted wife Halldóra, willing to bandage the wounded, whether foe or friend, but who reaps only the reproof of Glúm for saving his enemy Thórarin's life, and the peppery, sharp-tongued soothsayer Oddbjörg.

In conformity with the highly aristocratic notions of Old Icelandic society Glúm is credited with distinguished forebears among the first settlers of the island in the male line and with a lordly race in Norway on the distaff side. Treading in his departed father's footsteps, Glúm in his fifteenth year, feeling unable as yet to help his mother to fend off the aggression of Thorkel and his son Sigmund, betakes himself to Norway. There he meets his maternal grandfather, Vigfús, and is accepted by him as a scion of his race after ousting an intruding berserker. On Glúm's setting out for his homeland, Vigfús presents him with three heirlooms of the family, a cloak, a sword, and a spear, predicting that he will thrive while they are in his possession, but expressing the fear that parting with them will be his undoing. All this is told in the manner of the *Fornaldarsögur*, the "Tales of Olden Times." When Glúm sets foot on his home soil he discovers that his mother's estate has been still further encroached on by Sigmund and Thorkel having moved the boundary fence. After repeated entreaties of his mother he shakes off his torpor, drives Thorkel's trespassing cattle back into their owner's yard, and confronts their owner. That same fall he encounters Sigmund harvesting his own fertile field "Sure Giver" and slays him, thereby gaining the respect of the community, but at the same time the lasting enmity of the neighboring Esphœling people. And by the lawsuit following he acquires full possession of the parental estate of Thverá. He has come into his own now, and fortifies his leadership by an advantageous marriage and the acquisition of influential friends.

At this point there are several episodes in which Glúm plays rather a secondary role. They serve to enliven and give more substance to the story of his life. Their relative chronology is not known.

Arnór, a cousin of Glúm's, asks him to be an intermediary in his suit for the hand of Thórdís, the daughter of Gizur, Glúm's friend. She had previously been refused by her father to a certain wealthy and accomplished young man called Thorgrím. Knowing this, Glúm is unwilling to aid Arnór, but finally consents and, by the weight of his influence, causes Gizur to give Arnór the girl. Arnór is a merchant and has brought from overseas a load of malt and stored it by the shore of the fjord. He now goes to fetch it to be used in brewing ale for his wedding, but is ambushed by the rejected suitor Thorgrím. He himself escapes, but leaves the malt in Thorgrím's hands. At that, Glúm promptly gathers men to take revenge for the insult to his relative. However, he is met by an equal force of the Esphœling people. There is a compromise whereby Thorgrím is given another daughter of Gizur.

Much later, of course, the son of Arnór, Steinólf, and

the son of Thorgrím, Arngrím, are fostered together by their maternal grandmother, Saldís, and become inseparable. But a seeress predicts an evil end to their attachment. And this does come about, again much later, when Arngrím suspects his fosterbrother of having seduced his wife, and slays him. Arngrím later falls in the battle of Hrísateig between Glúm and the Esphœlings, largely provoked by this deed.

Enclosed within these events is the story of Ingólf. At a wrestling match Már, one of Glúm's sons, strikes up an acquaintance with him and procures him a job as overseer at the Thverá farm, to the satisfaction of Glúm. Ingólf had warned Már, that the stud he owns had caused mischief before. During a horse fight a certain man, Kálf of Stokkahlaða,[2] whose stallion was losing against Ingólf's, strikes Ingólf with his goading stick—a mortal insult in Old Iceland; but Már assures him that his father will see to it that he will not be shamed by the blow. Much to Glúm's displeasure Ingólf has become involved in a love affair with the daughter of farmer Thorkel, and frequently absents himself from Thverá. Thus one evening Ingólf returns home when all the household had finished their meal. For entertainment, Glúm suggests that every one name his *fulltrúi*, one in whom one places absolute trust; and to start the ball rolling, mentions as his own *fulltrúi* his purse, his battle-axe, and his barn or storehouse, then calls on Ingólf to do the same, and Ingólf chooses Thorkel; whereupon Glúm, angered, makes Ingólf accompany him to the barn. There he slaughters a calf, hands Ingólf the bloody sword, and bids him go to Thorkel with it and tell him that he has killed Hlöðu-Kálf (Barn-Calf), and ask him for his protection. He does as he is bidden, and Thorkel shows him the door. On his return to Thverá Glúm asks Ingólf how his *fulltrúi* had turned out, and he admits: "Not so well." (Of course, Glúm had meanwhile slain Kálf). He is sent abroad by Glúm who, later, at the Court procedure against him reveals the true facts and thus quashes the suit against Ingólf.

Nearly a hundred years ago a Swedish scholar, G. Cederschiöld, perceived that the story of Ingólf resembled a parable told by the Spanish Jew Petrus Alphonsi in his *Disciplina Clericalis,* written in the first part of the twelfth century, one of the most pilfered books of the Middle Ages. There exist two translations of it into Old Icelandic —unfortunately we do not know when made. The story runs as follows:

On his deathbed an Arab calls for his son and asks him how many friends he has, and the son replies that he has hundreds. The father entreats him not to trust a friend before having made a test of him. He himself claims to have won only one half friend in all his long life, and he advises his son to try his friends by slaughtering a calf and putting the carcass into a bag and then going to one of his friends, telling him he had killed a man and asking him to help to bury the corpse. The son does as instructed, but all his friends turn him away. Then the father asks him to go to his half friend and see what he says. And the half friend right away offers him his help.

Unquestionably there are here a number of palpable resemblances to the story of Ingólf. At the same time, as the Norwegian folklorist Knut Liestöl has justly observed, there are also differences; which would be cleared away if one took cognizance of the fact that there existed a number of variants of the fable, especially when one considers that there must have been some admixture of contemporaneous Icelandic events.

This problem was taken up by the Icelandic scholar Björn Sigfússon, who was able to show that certain events which took place in the North Quarter, precisely in the Eyjafjörð District, not so many years before our saga presumably was written (ca. 1225), show a striking resemblance to some details in the Ingólf story.[3]

However that may be, we cannot but admire the skill with which the author adapted the fable to the Icelandic milieu with its horse fights, wrestling matches, and the entertainment of choosing a *fulltrúi.*—Note also that by using the ruse he lets Glúm achieve several ends: he avenges the blow Kálf gave his protégé while at the same time deflecting the onus for Kálf's death on Ingólf, whom he manages to ship abroad; additionally he hopes to cure, or at least cool, Ingólf's infatuation, and he teaches him a lesson on whom he can, or cannot, depend as his *fulltrúi.*

With better reason we may consider the episode of Glúm's encounter with Víga-Skúta (Chapter 16) as an interpolation, chiefly because it is not integrated with other events in the saga, whereas in the *Reykdœla saga ok Víga-Skútu,* from which it appears loaned bodily, down to certain phrases, the separation of Glúm's daughter, Thorlaug, from Skúta (which causes the hostility between the two champions) is far more realistically described: there, Glúm actually plots the separation so that his daughter may make a better match.—There is also the curious circumstance that Thorlaug is not mentioned in our saga (Chapter 17) as one of Glúm's children, but only in the suspiciously brief passage explaining why she separates from Skúta: the daughters of high-ranking personages were an important asset. Marrying them to sons of influential families served to aggrandize one's own power.—And finally, whoever wrote the story of the encounter does not seem to have had the detailed knowledge of the topography of the district shown by the person who wrote the remainder of our saga, who no doubt was a native there.

This brings us to the question who that author might have been. Hardly a cleric, though of course clerically trained in the art of writing, or he would most likely have made disapproving remarks about Frey worship as against the practice of the true faith, and to have noted, however briefly, Thverá's becoming a monastery in later years. He would have had words of disapproval of Thorlaug's separation from her husband and her twice remarrying, all without benefit of clergy. His intimate knowledge of the lands and farms of the Eyjafjörð District and his knowledge of their owners would tend to show that he belonged to that class himself. He evidently had a vivid imagination and the dramatist's ability to enter into the feelings of others and express their thoughts, witness the disproportionate amount of direct speech, even in cases where the sense could have been conveyed as well, or better, by a few words in plain narrative. Yet the reader will note a goodly number of pungent replies. I mention as a little jewel the altercation between tart and aggressive Oddbjörg and the gentle, conciliatory Saldís.

In conformity with the realistic atmosphere in the body of the saga the supernatural is held to a minimum—the magic cloak, the gold-inlaid spear, and the sword given Glúm by his maternal grandfather which, we are told, are inseparable from their owner's good fortunes. To the world of dreams, though based on popular belief, belong the visions Glúm has of Valkyries and the wraith of his grandfather Vigfús to which Glúm refers in his verses.

In this connection it may be pointed out that it is not easy to have a definite opinion of Glúm's proficiency in the difficult art of skaldship[4] from the restricted amount of material handed down in the saga. That it was at least respectable we can infer from Snorri's quoting four separate passages of it in his *Edda*.

Our saga is handed down completely only in the *Möðruvallabók*, a huge compilation of various sagas, which was written down during the first half of the fourteenth century. Besides, there are only inconsiderable fragments. The translation here offered follows the text of Jónas Kristjánsson in his edition of *Eyfirðinga sögur*, Reykjavík, 1956. It is available also in G. Turville-Petre's edition, Oxford, Clarendon Press, 1960.

We append, as a kind of sequel, the *Story of Ögmund Dytt*, which shares with our saga the characters of its hero and his exiled son, Vigfús. This story is incorporated in its entirety in the *Expanded Saga of King Óláf Tryggvason*, where it is found among the legends and tales clustering around that missionary king, who ruled Norway from 995 to 1000.

L. M. H.

The University of Texas

Víga-Glúm's Saga

Chapter 1

A certain man was called Ingjald. He was the son of Helgi the Lean[1] and lived at Thverá farm in the Eyjafjörð District. He was a great chieftain, and *goði* of one of the original temple districts,[2] and of quite an advanced age at the time when the events of this saga took place. He was married and had two sons, Steinólf and Eyjólf, both handsome and accomplished men. Ingjald himself was self-willed, a man of few words, hard to deal with, and headstrong. He disliked merchants, not wishing to be subject to their arrogance. When he required something from them, he sent others to deal with them instead of going himself.

One summer a ship landed in the Eyjafjörð. The name of its skipper was Hreiðar, a man of noble birth. He had an estate at Vors[3] in Norway, and was a most valiant and well-liked man. Eyjólf that summer often came to his ship, and he and Hreiðar became fast friends. Hreiðar told

Eyjólf that he would like to stay in the Eyjafjörð District during the winter, declaring that he was most eager to take lodgings with Ingjald, having heard much good about him from others. Eyjólf explained to him that his father had not made it a practice to accommodate people, but said that he would see about it. And when he returned home he mentioned it to his father and said that he should invite the skipper, declaring him to be an honorable man and one of great worth, and spoke highly of him.

Ingjald answered: "If you have invited him already, then what is the use of my talking against it, and then I shall have to defray the expenses. But it will be your obligation to take care of him." He added that he had never had a foreigner in his house and still was reluctant to have one.

Eyjólf replied: "As yet he is not taken in and shall not be without your consent. But I will say that, so far, I have not had much to say about matters, and that you don't want me to have, if now you refuse to show hospitality to the man I have invited."

Ingjald answered: "Very well, I shall let you arrange matters as you wish and have the skipper come here, he and one other man. Also, for your sake, I shall not ill use him; but it will be your responsibility to look out for them. I shall bear the expenses." Eyjólf said that would suit him well.

The next day he went to look up Hreiðar and told him how matters stood. Hreiðar expressed his pleasure and had all his merchandise moved to Thverá farm. A short time later he observed that preparations were being made for a large-scale Yule celebration there. Ingjald was cool to him, but not unfriendly.

One day Hreiðar called Ingjald out to the shed where he had stored his wares, and Ingjald came with him. Then

Hreiðar asked him to choose from his goods whatever he liked. Ingjald declared that he wanted none of his goods, but said that he behaved handsomely.

Hreiðar declared: "Still I have thought of something that might be acceptable to you. I have visited several farms here in the Eyjafjörð District which are accounted among the best. But I have not seen any lodgings to compare with yours. However, your wall hangings are hardly superior to those in other farms." Thereupon he took out of his chests tapestries than which no finer ones had till that time been brought to Iceland, and these he gave to Ingjald. Ingjald thanked him very much, and from that time on they were on the best of terms.

Later in the winter Eyjólf said to Hreiðar that he would like to go abroad with him when spring came.[4] He was slow to answer. Eyjólf said: "Why won't you take me along? Don't you like me?" "Very well indeed," Hreiðar answered; "however, your father would think I repaid him poorly for his hospitality, and I don't mean to do so, by taking along his son who is such a credit to him in every way. But if your father has no objections I shall be glad to take you along and shall indeed be pleased to do so then."

The merchants made their preparations for the journey, and when they were ready Eyjólf again inquired whether Hreiðar cared to take him abroad with him. Hreiðar informed him of his decision not to act in opposition to his father's wishes in taking him abroad. Thereupon Eyjólf told his father about his eagerness to see the world, and also how matters stood between him and Hreiðar. Ingjald said there were few men as upright as Hreiðar, "and because of your conduct in this matter and his proven uprightness I shall allow you to go, and indeed think it is better for you to go with him than with others."

19

Chapter 2

Thereupon they left Iceland and landed in Norway. Hreiðar made Eyjólf many proposals about finding quarters,
but he would not accept any he suggested. Hreiðar asked:
"Then what are your intentions?"

He replied: "I don't know."

Hreiðar said: "Aren't you eager to join the king or other
chieftains? You may depend on our support"—at that time
Hákon,[5] the fosterson of King Aðalstein [Aethelstan],
ruled over Norway.—"It would seem desirable for people
of high birth such as you are to serve such chieftains and
be their willing retainers."

Eyjólf replied: "I am not fit to be the retainer of
kings, although that might be according to my wishes.
Yet I am unwilling."

"Then what do you mean to do?" asked Hreiðar.

"Why do you hesitate to invite me to your own place,
because that is what I would like."

"I have little mind to do that," replied Hreiðar.

"What can be the reason for that?" asked Eyjólf.

Hreiðar replied: " I don't care to offer what would not

be good for you to accept, since you deserve only good from me."

"I wonder what can be the reason for that?" asked Eyjólf.

"That you shall hear, though it ill befits me to tell you. I have a brother. His name is Ívar. Together we own an estate and all the properties belonging to it, and we are very fond of each other. However, we are unlike each other in that he dislikes Icelanders, so much so that they can't be put up there. He is away on Viking expeditions every summer, and when he returns he has with him some nine or eleven men, and they expect every one in the establishment to be at their beck and call; and they all would treat you so badly that you couldn't stand it at all."

Eyjólf answered: "I am curious how they would behave, and I shall not hold it against you if you will grant me your hospitality."

Hreiðar replied: "I am under obligation to my brother, who always brings me gifts, the finest he can obtain; so we won't fall out about you; but I would be sorry for you if they jeer and mock at you."

"You seem very reluctant to have me as your guest," said Eyjólf. "For that matter, how will Ívar behave toward me? He certainly will not try to strike me?"

Hreiðar answered: "It would be worse than a thrashing; he has many a wicked man in his company, and they are likely to misconstrue whatever you say or do."

Eyjólf said: "That won't be any mortification if one is told about it beforehand. It is unwise not to put up with that sort of thing, and that won't be any hindrance."

Hreiðar replied: "In that case I am in a quandary: you are my friend, and he is my brother, of whom I am very fond."

21

In the end Eyjólf went with Hreiðar and took winter quarters there in Vors. And when Ívar was expected there, Eyjólf wore a fur cloak every day. He was a large man and always sat by Hreiðar's side.

Chapter 3

Toward Yule Ívar returned home, was met honorably, and welcomed in a kindly manner. Then each asked the other for news, and where Hreiðar had spent the past winter. He replied that he had wintered in Iceland.

Thereupon Ívar asked for no further news. "But is that thing by your side a man or a beast? It certainly is no small hulk."

Eyjólf made answer: "I am an Icelander, and my name is Eyjólf, and I intend to stay here during the winter." "If that is so then I am thinking," said Ívar, "that there will be some mishap on this estate if an Icelander is to stay here."

Hreiðar answered: "If you mistreat him so that he can't stay, then it will be all the worse for us as kinsmen."

"In that case," said Ívar, "it was on an evil day that you went to Iceland if on that account we are to wait on Icelanders or else forego our kinsmen and friends. And I can't understand why you like to consort with the worst of people. Also, you need not tell me any of your experiences there."

"Quite on the contrary," said Hreiðar, "there are fairly many excellent people there."

Ívar said: "Anyway, that thickset, raggedy fellow in the highseat isn't exactly an ornament."

But as Ívar understood that his brother appeared to make much of this man he railed less against Icelanders. "But what," he said, "should I call him, a hulk?"

Eyjólf declared he did not mind that name at all. But whatever he did or said they misconstrued.

A certain man called Vigfús was a hersir[6] who ruled the district of Vors. He was the son of Sigurð, the son of Víkinga-Kári. He had a daughter called Ástríð. He and the brothers Ívar and Hreiðar were great friends. Each in turn celebrated Yule with the other, and this year the brothers were to prepare the Yule feast at their place. Hreiðar had prepared everything and was then ready to invite people.

He asked Eyjólf to come with him,[7] saying: "And I am not eager to find out how they [Ívar's men] will treat you."

Eyjólf said: "I don't feel well, and I shall not go with you."

The same evening that Hreiðar had left and Ívar's followers had taken their seats at table in the hall they said: "Now Hulk is here and Hreiðar is not. Now we shall have some entertainment, the way we like to." Ívar said: "However, let us consider what befits us. Here we two brothers own this property between us, and Hreiðar has the care of it all, and I not any. Now then, here is a man to whom he wishes to show hospitality, and we behave in such a fashion that he can hardly stay here. However, he has done us no harm, and no one is to say anything to offend him while Hreiðar is not here."

They said that then it was an opportune time to have

some sport. Ívar replied: "You talk like churls. Here every one is at your beck and call, and we have sport with everything as we please, when others have the work and the care. Now even if this man had killed my brother I would not harm him, so as not to offend Hreiðar. And I will not tolerate that any one is to make sport of him, and he is not to be called Hulk any longer."

On the next morning Ívar asked Eyjólf whether he cared to go to the woods with them to have some pastime. He said he did, and so he went with them, and they felled trees and transported them to the farm. Eyjólf had his sword and a small axe with him. Ívar said: "Icelander, I advise you that in case every one goes his own way, that you go home before it gets dark."

Then every one went his own way through the forest, and Eyjólf too. He took off his fur cloak and laid the sword, which he had carried in his hand, upon it. He then walked into the woods to have some sport. With his axe he felled trees that seemed to him good timber. But as the day wore on it began to snow; so he wanted to return; he retraced his steps to the spot where his fur cloak had lain, but found it gone, but not the sword. He observed that the snow had been swept away where his cloak had been dragged. A brown bear[8] had been there and had dragged off the cloak, but had scarcely had the strength to lift it. Eyjólf reasoned that it was a cub which had just left its lair and had not killed a man as yet. He followed the track and saw it sitting before him. He drew his sword and cut off the snout close to the eyes and brought it back to the farm with him.

Ívar had returned earlier and, missing Eyjólf, said: "We have behaved improperly, leaving our companion behind. He doesn't know his way in the woods. There are likely to be many dangerous beasts there, and people will make remarks about it if he doesn't return when he had been with us before. And I advise that we search for him till we find him." But as they came out of doors, Eyjólf met them. Ívar welcomed him cordially and asked why there was blood on his clothes, and he showed them what he had in his hand.

Then Ívar said: "I am afraid that you are wounded."

Eyjólf answered: "Be of good cheer, nothing ails me."

Then Ívar said: "It is foolish to make fun of people one doesn't know. He has shown valor in this deed, one which I doubt if any one of us would dare to perform."

On the next evening Hreiðar returned. Ívar said: "Why are you so silent, brother? Are you anxious about that man Hulk? What do you fear I have contrived against him?"

Hreiðar replied: "It will certainly make a difference in our relations to know what you have done."

"What if I tell you that I feel toward him as you do?"

Hreiðar answered: "I shall give you the gold ring which both of us own and which you prize so highly."

Ívar replied: "I do not covet your patrimony; I value Eyjólf as highly as you do, and he is to sit by me now and not by you." Then both showed him great honor and saw to it that his seat at table was well furnished. And so time passed.

Chapter 4

Now the guests arrived for the Yule banquet at the brothers' place. And when it was arranged who should sit and drink with whom,[9] and lots were cast who should sit next to Ástríð, the daughter of Hersir Vigfús, Eyjólf each time was so lucky as to sit by her side; but no one saw them talk more to each other than to others. Still, many were of the opinion that it would probably turn out that she was destined to be his wife. The feast then came to an end. It had been celebrated in a grand manner, and the participants were each given a farewell present.

Eyjólf spent four summers going on viking expeditions and was considered most daring and valiant. He achieved fame and gained much booty.

One winter a man named Thorstein came to Vors. He was a kinsman of the two brothers there and had an estate in the Upplands district. He told them of the difficulties he had with a berserker named Ásgaut, who had challenged him to a duel because he had refused to let him have his sister; and now Thorstein requested

the brothers to accompany him with a number of followers to the scene of the duel in order to prevent this
marauder from encroaching on his property, adding that
Ásgaut had even killed many of his men and that he
would lose his sister unless they supported him. "I don't
trust myself to fight this duel if I don't have the benefit
of your luck."[10] They did not find it in their hearts to
refuse to accompany him.

They proceeded with him to the Upplands with thirty
men till they arrived at the place where they were to meet
Ásgaut. Then they inquired among their men who would
dare to fight with Ásgaut and thus win a bride. But
although the woman seemed desirable, no one appeared
ready to run the risk. Then the two brothers asked Eyjólf
to hold the shield over Thorstein.[11] Eyjólf replied that
he had never done that for any one and that no one had
done that for himself. "And it would not seem good to
me if he were slain while I was shielding him. I see no
honor gained in doing that. And if this young man was
slain while I was shielding him, shall we then return
home as matters would stand then? Or shall we have to
find another man to fight with Ásgaut and still another?
Our discomfiture will be the greater the more of us fall.
Little honor will we have gained on our journey if we
return without having avenged Thorstein, in case he falls.
Rather, ask me to fight with this berserker. That is what
one owes one's friends; but hold the shield for Thorstein
I shall not."

They thanked him cordially although they thought he
was running a great risk.

He said: "I believe that no one of us will escape with
his life unless we avenge Thorstein; and it would seem
worse to have to fight that berserker, once your kinsman
is slain."

Then he stepped forward, and Ívar volunteered to hold the shield over him.

Eyjólf made this reply: "Nobly offered, but this is my affair. And the old saying holds good that one's own hands are most reliable."

Thereupon he proceeded to the place appointed for the duel. The berserker said: "Is that big fellow to fight me?"

Eyjólf replied: "Isn't it so that you are afraid to fight with me? Maybe you aren't really such a hero since you lose heart when you are to fight with a big man, but bluster when you have to do with a little one."

"That doesn't apply to me," he replied; "but now I am going to inform you of the regulations of the duel: with the payment of three marks I shall absolve myself from the duel if I am wounded."

Eyjólf answered: "I don't feel obliged to observe your regulations since you now put an estimate on what you are worth; because in our country that would be considered the wergild payable for killing a thrall, which now you would award to yourself."

Eyjólf was to deal the first blow, and with it the point of Ásgaut's shield was sheared off, together with his foot. For this deed Eyjólf earned much praise, and thereupon returned to the brothers' estate. Much property was offered him now, but he said he had not done this for gain nor to acquire a bride but solely out of friendship with the brothers. Ásgaut absolved himself from the duel with money, and from that time on was a cripple.

Later, Eyjólf asked for the hand of Vigfús's daughter Ástríð. Ívar and Hreiðar offered to support his suit. They declared him to be of noble birth and to hold a high position in Iceland and to have the support of many kinsmen, and also that he had expectations of a considerable patrimony.

Then Eyjólf spoke up: "Very possibly Ástríð's kinsmen will consider my suit presumptuous, but many in Iceland know that I have noble ancestry and large properties."

Vigfús said: "That then is likely to be her settlement for marriage, though no less a match had been intended for our kinswoman." So she was betrothed to him and sailed to Iceland with him.

Chapter 5

Böðvar was the name of a son of Víkinga-Kári and a brother of Sigurð, the father of Vigfús. This Böðvar was the father of Ástríð, the mother of Eirík (the son of King Harald Fairhair of Norway). Eirík had a daughter also named Ástríð, who became the mother of King Óláf Tryggvason. Víkinga-Kári was the son of Eymund Akra-spillir (Field-Destroyer),[12] the son of Thórir; and Böðvar was the father of Ólof, the mother of Gizur the White.

At the time Eyjólf and his wife Ástríð landed in Iceland Ingjald had died. Thereupon Eyjólf took over his estate and the goði authority. Úlfeið, Ingjald's daughter, was married to Hríseyjar-Narfi.

Eyjólf and Ástríð had four children, of whom Thorstein was the oldest. He was paid his share of the inheritance left by Ingjald when he married. He lived at Hólar in the Eyjafjörð district during the remainder of his life and has little to do with this story. Another son, Vigfús, was married to Hallfríð, the daughter of Thorkel the Tall from Lake Mývatn. Glúm was their youngest son. There was also a daughter, Helga, who was married to Steingrím of

31

Sigluvík. Their son was Thorvald, nicknamed Tasaldi, who later comes into this story. Vigfús died a short time after his marriage. He had a child which did not survive him long; and for this reason Hallfríð inherited half of all the property, the other half going to Glúm and Ástríð. By this time Eyjólf had died, whereupon Thorkel the Tall and his son Sigmund moved to Thverá. Sigmund was a man of note. He had the idea that he might become a chieftain if by making a good match he gained the support of additional kinsmen.

There was a certain man called Thórir who dwelled at Espihól. He was the son of Hámund Darkskin and of Ingunn, daughter of Helgi the Lean. He was married to Thordís, daughter of Kaðal. Their children were Thórarin, Thorvald Barb, who lived at Grund in the Eyjafjörð district, Thorgrím, who lived at Möðrufell, Ingunn, who was married to Thórð, the Priest of Frey, and Vígdís, she who married Sigmund.

A short time later, Thorkel and his son Sigmund took to harassing Ástríð, so the land was partitioned, Glúm and Ástríð retaining that half which had no houses on it. They then set up their farm on Borgarhól Hill.

Glúm was not interested in farming and in general seemed rather slow to develop. He was taciturn and reserved, most of the time. He was tall and somewhat swarthy of complexion, fairhaired and straight-haired, of slender build, and considered rather slow-witted. He did not frequent meetings of men. With Thorkel and Sigmund bearing down on them, Ástríð's and Glúm's possessions began to dwindle, and they were getting the worst in every deal.

A sanctuary dedicated to the god Frey was located south of the river[13] at Hripkelsstaðir. Thórarin, the farmer at Espihól, was a man both wise and well liked. Thorvald

Barb, his brother, however, was a duelist and apt to provoke a quarrel. Sigmund, the son of Thorkel, was considered a man of substance after he had married into the family at Espihól.

Glúm told his mother that he wanted to go abroad, saying: "I realize that I can't get along here; but it may be that I shall prosper from visiting with my distinguished kinsman in Norway. I can't put up with the aggressive ways of Sigmund, still I am not, as yet, capable of opposing him. Don't let go of our land though your lot is made hard by them."—Glúm was fifteen years old when he was thus eager to go abroad.

Chapter 6

Now to tell about Glúm's travels abroad. As soon as he landed in Norway he betook himself to Vors[13a] to pay his respects to Vigfús. As he approached the estate he observed that there was a great crowd engaged in many kinds of pastimes and sports, and he gathered that the place was one of great munificence in every respect; and seeing many distinguished-looking men he did not know who of them might be his kinsman Vigfús. But this was how he recognized him: he saw a large and distinguished-looking man in the high-seat. He was clad in a hooded cloak of black fur and amused himself playing with a gold-inlaid spear. Glúm went up to him and greeted him. The man took his greeting kindly and asked him who he might be. Glúm replied that he was an Icelander and from the Eyjafjörð District. Thereupon Vigfús asked him about his son-in-law Eyjólf and his daughter Ástríð, and was told that Eyjólf had died: "But Ástríð is still living." Then he asked who were their children, and Glúm told him of his brothers and sisters, and then informed him that one of their sons was standing before him. But after he had said that the conversation ended. Glúm asked him where he was to sit at table; but Vigfús said he did not know whether to believe what Glúm had told him, and assigned him a seat on the lower bench near the door, thus showing him little honor. Glúm was taciturn and unsociable. When the others drank or had some other entertainment he lay there with his cloak over his head. He was thought to be only a fool.

A banquet was prepared at the beginning of winter and a sacrifice made to the *dísir*,[14] and all present were to take part in these rites. Glúm remained sitting in his seat and did not come forward. And as the evening wore on and all were present, there did not prevail such high spirits as might have been expected, considering the good entertainment and the gathering of friends, many of whom had come to this meeting. And on the day people assembled for the banquet Glúm did not leave the house to welcome them, nor did he invite any one to sit by his side or in his seat.

Now when every one was seated at the table the news was passed around that a man called Björn, and nicknamed Iron-skull, had come to the estate with eleven other men. He was a great berserker, accustomed to come to meetings attended by many people, where he would start arguments with men to see whether any one would make a statement to which he would take exception, and then challenge him to a duel. Vigfús asked his guests to be careful about their speech, "because that is less of a humiliation than to suffer great evil from him," and they all promised to be so.

Björn went into the hall, expecting to be welcomed. Beginning with the higher bench, he asked the man sitting nearest to the door if he considered himself his equal. He said: "By no means." Then Björn asked one after another that question, until he came to the high-seat. Various answers were given him, but the upshot was always that no one considered himself his equal. But when he got to Vigfús he asked him where he knew the equal of such dauntless men as himself and his companions, and Vigfús admitted he did not know their equal. Then Björn said: "That was a good answer and a wise one, as could be expected. You are a man of great distinction, and your life has been spent as you most desired, and you have suffered no check to your honor and dignity. Now it is well that I don't need to say anything but good to you; but one thing I do want to ask you: do you consider yourself my equal?" Vigfús answered: "When I was a young man and on viking expeditions, winning distinction, I would have said so; but now I don't know whether I might be called your equal, and far less so, now that I am old and infirm."

Björn then turned away from him and proceeded along the lower bench, to a place near the door asking the men there whether they considered themselves his equals, and they said they did not. Then he came to where Glúm lay on the raised floor. "Why does this man lie there instead of sitting up?" he inquired. Glúm's neighbors on the bench made answer for him, explaining that he was such a fool that it made no difference what he said. Björn kicked him and said that he should sit up like the others, and asked him whether he considered himself his equal. Glúm said that he did not need to pick on him and that he didn't know about his valor. "And as to considering myself your equal, I wouldn't do that, because in Iceland a man would be called a fool who conducted himself as you do. But I have noticed that here everybody knows how to moderate himself in his replies to you." And with that he jumped up and made a rush at Björn.

He tore his helmet off, and grabbing a fire brand, poked it between his shoulders, so the berserk cringed before the blow, and hit him again and again till he fell. And when he wanted to regain his feet he struck him on the head, and kept on doing that till the man got outside.

When Glúm wanted to return to his seat, Vigfús and all the others left theirs; and then Vigfús welcomed his kinsman cordially, declaring that he had furnished proof that he belonged to his kin, "and I shall honor you as befits us both." He added that the reason for his former behavior was that he, Glúm, did not appear to give promise of early development: "So I decided to wait until you vindicated your kinship with our family by some deed of prowess." Then he conducted him to the seat by his side. Glúm declared that he would accept that seat, and would have done so before if it had been offered to him.

On the following day the death of Björn was made known. Vigfús offered Glúm to take over his own authority and rank on his demise, and Glúm said he would assume that. But first he would sail to Iceland to prevent those men from taking over his patrimony to whom he was loath to grant it, but that he would return as soon as possible. Vigfús said he thought it Glúm's destiny to increase the power and the distinction of his family in Iceland.

The following summer Vigfús had a ship made ready for Glúm, giving him the cargo on it, together with much wealth in gold and silver, and said: "I have a premonition that we shall not see each other again. These family heirlooms will I give you, a cloak, a spear, and a sword in which our kinsmen have had much faith; and while you are in possession of these valuables I expect that you will not lose your position of honor. But I fear you will if you let go of them." With that they parted.

Chapter 7

Now Glúm sailed to Iceland and at once proceeded to his home at Thverá. He rejoined his mother right away, and she gave him a hearty welcome. She told him of the wrongs done her by Thorkel and Sigmund. He bade her have patience, saying that as yet he was little capable of resisting them. Then he rode home to his farmstead. There he observed that the fence[15] had been moved and his land encroached on. Then he spoke a verse:

> 1) Nearer to me, necklace-
> Nanna,[16] and to all my
> meinie,[16a] moved is the sod-wall—
> mournful am I—than looked for:
> pushed off my patrimony
> pitylessly, here I
> tell it; nor shall I turn from
> tumult-of-steel,[17] deedless.

This had happened while Glúm was abroad: Sigmund had encroached on Ástríð's land and had the intention of depriving her of her place of residence. One fall, while

38

Glúm was abroad, two heifers were found to be missing out of Thorkel and Sigmund's herd, and they suspected that they had been stolen. They suspected that some of Ástríð's thralls had stolen them and asserted that they had eaten them secretly, and summoned them for the theft. As it happened, these very thralls were by far the most devoted servants Ástríð had for work and supervising, and she feared she could hardly maintain herself on her farm without them. So she had gone to her son Thorstein and told him how Thorkel and Sigmund were bearing down on her, and asked him to defend the thralls. "I would rather pay damages for what they have done," she said, "than have them outlawed on false charges, if there is no other way out; and I think you ought to be my shield and protection and thus prove yourself member of a good family."

Thorstein replied that he expected that Thorkel and Sigmund would rely on the support of their kinsmen in pressing their suit. "And it would seem advisable to me—if, indeed, these men are indispensable for you to maintain yourself on your farm—that we do all we can in the case and pay the damages rather than have them outlawed or exiled."

She answered: "I am afraid they will impose stiff penalties such as will be of lasting damage to me. But because there is little help to be expected from you it seems unavoidable to submit to their decision in the case."

Among the prized possessions that went with the Thverá estate the greatest was the field Vitazgjafi,[18] so called because it never failed to produce a harvest. Now when the Thverá land was partitioned it was done in such fashion that each party should have that field every other summer. So now Ástríð went to Thorkel and Sigmund and said: "It is evident that you are planning to ruin me utterly because you observe that there is no leadership here. But rather than give up my thralls I would submit the matter to your judgment." They called that a wiser counsel and laid their plans accordingly. And it was their decision to demand sole right of judgment over the thralls or else declare them outlawed.

Thorstein on his part was so slack in defending the thralls that Thorkel and Sigmund obtained the right of self-judgment and had themselves awarded the field as their sole possession; and they intended in this manner to get hold of all of Ástríð's land, thus depriving her of most of her sustenance. That very summer she was to have use of the field by stipulation. But also that summer, at the time people flocked to the Assembly,[19] a herdsman walking about the pasture found the heifers buried under a landslide which then at the beginning of winter had been covered over by drifting snow. So the slander against the thralls stood revealed. Now when Thorkel and his son learned that the heifers had been found, they offered money to pay for the field but refused to surrender their rights to it. But Ástríð declared that she wouldn't get overmuch redress for the slander if she merely regained her property, "and I demand to have what is my own, or else lose it altogether. And if no one will see to it that justice is done I shall bide my time in the expectation that Glúm will return and set matters to rights." Sigmund remarked: "Late or never will *he* plough a furrow, whilst that one of the your sons stands by and does nothing who would be more likely to act." She replied: "Pride often cometh before a fall, Sigmund, and so does injustice, and maybe that this will happen to you."

A little later that summer Glúm arrived in Iceland. He stayed but a short time by his ship, then proceeded to his farm with a wealth of possessions. He showed the

40

same temperament as when he left the country: he was reserved and behaved as though he had not learned what had happened at his home while he was abroad. Every day he slept till forenoon and did not attend to the business of the farm. It was the summer he and his mother were to have the use of the field Vitazgjafi if matters had gone according to rights. But Sigmund's cattle did great damage, grazing every morning in her home meadow.

One morning Ástríð waked Glúm, saying that Sigmund's herd of cattle had come into the home meadow and were about to pull down the haystacks, "and I am not quick enough to drive them away, and our workmen are busy." He replied: "Rarely have you called me to work, and I shall not resent it that you do so now." And with that he jumped out of bed, mounted his horse and, with a cudgel in his hand, vigorously drove the cattle away, striking them again and again until they arrived on Thorkel's and Sigmund's home meadow where he let them do all the damage they wanted.

Thorkel was accustomed to watch the haystacks, mornings on the farm, while Sigmund was at work with the servants. Thorkel said to Glúm: "You can expect that people won't put up with your damaging their cattle, even though you may have won distinction abroad."

Glúm said that as yet his cattle were not damaged, "but if they enter our property again and damage it, they won't escape altogether unhurt, and you will have to put up with it, nor will you be able to do anything about it, for we will not stand for any more damage from your cattle."

Then Thorkel said: "You talk big now, you Glúm, but you look to us like the same fool you were when you went abroad, and we won't let your chatter determine what we mean to do."

41

Glúm went home and fell to laughing. He was so agitated that he became pale, and there fell out of his eyes tears large as big-sized hailstones, and that is how he was often stirred in later times when the fighting spirit came upon him.

Chapter 8

We are told that as the autumn was drawing to a close, one morning Ástríð went to speak with Glúm. She waked him and requested him to go to work. She said that the hay-making would be finished if matters had been attended to as they should have been. And that Thorkel and his son had finished with it a short while ago. "Early this morning Sigmund and Vigdís, his wife, went to the field Vitazgjafi, and probably think it is theirs, while by rights it is ours."

Then Glúm got up, yet was not ready before late in the morning. Then he put on his dark blue fur cloak and seized his gold-inlaid spear. He had his horse saddled.

Ástríð then remarked: "Great pains you take today with your clothes for hay-making, my son."

He answered: "I don't often go to work, but when I do, then I shall both do a big piece of work and prepare myself well for it; and yet I don't know how to prepare myself well for this business. I shall now ride up to Hólar and accept my brother Thorstein's hospitality."

Thereupon he rode south and over the river. And when

he came to the field Vitazgjafi he took the clasp out of his cloak. Vigdís and Sigmund were working in the field. When Vigdís saw him, she walked up to him and bade him welcome. "We are sorry," she said "that we kinfolk are on such bad terms, and I shall do all in my power to improve our relations." Glúm said: "As yet nothing has occurred which would prevent our relationship being good. But the reason for my turning this way is that the clasp has come out of my cloak, and I would that you sew it on again." She said she would gladly do that; and so she did. Glúm let his eye sweep over the field and said: "Never yet has Vitazgjafi failed."

Thereupon he put the cloak over his shoulders, took his spear in hand and turned toward Sigmund, brandishing it. Sigmund leapt up to defend himself, but Glúm at once struck him on the head, and that was his deathblow.

Then he approached Vigdís and told her to go home, "and tell Thorkel that Sigmund is not able to leave the field by himself"; whereupon he rode up to Hólar. But he did not tell Thorstein what had occurred. When Thorstein noticed his equipment and his having both spear and cloak, he saw blood in the damascened ornaments of the spear blade and asked whether he had recently dealt a blow with it.

Glúm answered: "Oh yes, I forgot to tell you that I killed Sigmund Thorkelsson today."

Thorstein said: "That will indeed seem an important piece of news to them, to Thorkel and the people at Espihól, his kinsmen." Glúm answered: "It is an old saying that the blood nights are the fiercest.[20] They are apt to think it of little account as time passes on."

Glúm stayed three days with his kinfolk, and then made ready to return home. Thorstein offered to accompany him, but Glúm said that wasn't necessary: "Just you take

44

care of your farm.[21] I shall ride the direct way to Thverá. They are not apt to follow this up now." And so he rode home to Thverá.

When this news was heard Thorkel looked up Thórarin and asked for his advice how to proceed with the case. He said: "Maybe Ástríð will be saying now that Glúm had matured with a vengeance."

Thorkel replied: "This I think, that he has matured in such fashion that he won't proceed very far."[22] Thórarin answered: "That remains to be seen. You have long done them wrong and tried to ruin them, without anticipating what could be expected of the offspring of men like Eyjólf, who was both of noble race and a dauntless man. Also, we need to think of our ties of kinship with him, seeing that you are related to him by marriage. Again, the suit against him won't be an easy matter if he himself defends the case, as I presume he will."

Thereupon Thorkel went home, and nothing was done about the suit during the winter. Glúm kept somewhat more men about him than he was wont to in winter.

Chapter 9

We are told that one night Glúm had a dream: he dreamed
that he was standing outside of his farm, looking out
toward the fjord. And he thought he saw a woman come
from the fjord and proceed through the district, heading
toward Thverá. She was so huge that her shoulders
touched the mountains on either side. He dreamed that
he left his farm and went up to her to invite her in. Then
he awoke. This dream seemed strange to all he told it,
but he said this: "This dream is significant and notable;
and I would interpret it in this wise: Vigfús, my maternal
grandfather, very likely passed away, these days, and
this woman who walked there, taller than the mountains,
probably is his guardian spirit. He was more distinguished
than other men, and his guardian spirit likely is seek-
ing to take up her abode with me." And when ships from
Norway arrived there the following summer they brought
with them the news that Vigfús had died. Then Glúm
spoke this verse:

> 2. Methinks, that huge and helm-clad,
> hitherward a woman

proceeded swiftly, heading,
silver-dís,[23] toward Thverá,
high as the hills towering,
head-dress Frigg,[24] in my
dream I deemed her Oðin's
daughter,[25] warrior-choosing.

The following spring Thorkel went to see Thorvald
Barb and the other sons of Thórir and urged them to press
this suit, giving as his reason their own relation by marriage to Vigdís as well as many acts of friendship which
both he and his son Sigmund had done them.

Thorvald looked up Thórarin and said it would be
regarded as downright shameful if he and his kin did not
lend their support to the suit brought by their kinsman,
adding that he himself would assist them with all his re-
sources. "And it is quite evident that Glúm thinks he will
gain distinction by his having slain Sigmund. But we
won't concede to be his inferiors in the district." To this,
Thórarin replied: "It would seem to me that it might be
difficult so to press this suit so as to be sure to increase
our standing in the community. Moreover, considering
Glúm's added reputation, it is not unlikely that he takes
after his forebears. And I approach this business more
reluctantly than you because I am not sure who will have
the best of it if we contend with Glúm, and I wouldn't
like it if thereby we add to our discomfiture."

But what with the urging of Thorkel, Thórarin Thórisson did prepare a suit against Glúm, to be brought at
the General Assembly for the slaying of Sigmund. Glúm,
on his part, brought suit against Thorkel the Tall, charg-
ing him for slandering the thralls, and another against
Sigmund, accusing him of theft and stating that he was
killed on his (Glúm's) property and therefore was not

47

entitled to the protection of the law; and he dug Sigmund's body up.[26] Thereupon both these suits were entered at the General Assembly.

Glúm turned to his relatives, Gizur the White, the son of Ketilbjörn of Mosfell, and Ásgrím Elliðagrímsson, for support. He informed them how matters stood, about Thorkel's and Sigmund's acts of aggression and their unfair dealings with Ástríð, and how they had insulted him many times. He said he expected his kin to support him to obtain justice, but would conduct the suit himself. And they all declared that they owed it to him that he wasn't left at the mercy of his enemies. Also, that they were glad that one of their kin stood his ground.

Time passed till the court went into session, when the Esphœling people proceeded with their suit against Glúm, at the insistence of the family members whose concern it was to be mindful of the wrongs done against them; and it was presented in such fashion as to avoid any flaws. Glúm on his part entered his suit against Thorkel; and both suits were presented to the court. Glúm had much support from kinsmen and friends. And when the defense was called he had this to say: "This is how matters stand: it will be evident to many that you have entered your suit on the wrong premises and with a flaw in it, for I slew Sigmund on my own land; and before riding to the assembly[27] I charged him for a deed punishable by outlawry." And he called witnesses for his statement and thus defended his suit. And his kinsmen supported him so strongly that Sigmund was declared to have fallen as outlaw.

Thereupon Glúm proceeded with his suit against Thorkel for his attempt to obtain his (Glúm's) land unlawfully. And it looked bad for Thorkel, for all the witnesses came out in favor of Glúm, and no legal defenses for

Thorkel were entered. The outcome was that it appeared that Thorkel was going to be sentenced to outlawry. Then his adherents sought to come to terms with Glúm. Glúm insisted that there were only two possibilities: either, that he would proceed with his suit to the finish, or that Thorkel hand over to him Thverá farm at a price fixed by Glúm himself, and that was no more than half its value. "And if Thorkel is declared outlaw he might as well expect that only one of us will attend the Assembly next summer."[28]

Thereupon Thorkel's friends took a hand, advising him to come to terms, so Thorkel made the sensible decision to do so and sell Glúm the land. He (Thorkel) was to dwell on it that year. So then they were reconciled in name. But the Esphœling people were of course displeased with the outcome of the suit, and they were never thereafter fully reconciled with Glúm.

Before Thorkel left Thverá farm he went to the sanctuary of Frey, leading with him an old ox, and spoke as follows: "Frey," he said, "you have long been my patron, and have received many gifts from me and have rewarded them well: here I give you this ox, in order that Glúm may leave Thverá no less willingly than I leave it now. Let me have some sign whether or not you accept my gift." At that, the ox was so startled that he bellowed and fell down dead; and that, Thorkel took to mean that the godhead was well inclined, and he felt more at ease then, because he thought his sacrifice had been accepted. Later, he betook himself north to Lake Mývatn, where he settled; and he is now out of the saga.

Chapter 10

Glúm by now had achieved great respect in the district. A man called Gunnstein lived at Lón in Horgárdal. He was distinguished, wealthy, and counted among men of great influence. Hlíf was the name of his wife. Their son Thorgrím was called Hlífarson after his mother, the reason being that she lived longer than Gunnstein. She was a most outstanding woman. Thorgrím was well bred and became a man of distinction. Another son of theirs was Grím, nicknamed Eyrarlegg. Halldóra, their daughter, was a handsome woman of good disposition. She was considered an excellent match because of her influential relatives, but chiefly because of her own ability and efficiency. Glúm sought her hand, claiming that it was hardly necessary to mention his connections and his line, nor his possessions and conduct. "All this is probably known to you. But I have chosen this match for myself, her kinsmen consenting." His suit was well received, and she was betrothed to him with a big dowry, and their marriage celebrated appropriately. So now his state of life was even more distinguished than before.

A certain man was called Thorvald, the son of Ref. He lived at Bárð in the Fljót District. He was married to Thuríð, the daughter of Thórð of Höfði. Their children were a son, Klaufi, and a daughter, Thorgerð, who was the wife of Thórarin of Espihól. Thorvald Barb at Grund farm was married to Thorkatla from Thjórsárdal. Hlenni the Old, the son of Örnólf Toskubak dwelled at Viðiness and was married to Oddkatla, the daughter of Oddkel from Thjórsárdal. Gizur Kaðalsson is also mentioned. He lived at Tjarnir in the Eyjafjarðardal. His wife was Saldís, an excellent housewife. Gizur also belonged among the most influential and wealthy farmers. He had two daughters, Thordís and Herthrúð, both handsome and showy persons, who were considered good matches. They grew up on the paternal farm. Gizur's brother was called Rúnólf, and he was the father of Valgerð, the mother of Eyjólf of Möðruvellir. Thordís was the daughter of Kaðal and was married to Thórir of Espihól—their children were mentioned above.

Thorgrím, the son of Thórir, was not the son of his wife, Thórdís, although legitimate. Thorgrím was an important and accomplished personage. He looked up Gizur for the purpose of asking for his daughter in marriage. Supporting his suit were his brothers, friends, and kinsmen of the girl. They considered themselves entitled to have a say in the disposal of their kinswoman, and they thought the proposal altogether auspicious. His suit was refused, however, although every one considered Thorgrím her equal in every respect. His brothers and kinsmen were much disgruntled by this.

Chapter 11

A certain man called Arnór, nicknamed Redcheek, now comes into the saga. He was the son of Steinólf, who was the son of Ingjald, and thus a first cousin of Glúm. He had been on merchant expeditions for a long time and was highly regarded. Winters he always stayed with Glúm when in Iceland. He proposed to Glúm that he should ask for a woman's hand for him. Glúm asked what woman he had in mind. Arnór said: "Thordís, the daughter of Gizur, the one who was refused to Thorgrím, the son of Thórir." Glúm replied: "This does not seem very hopeful to me, because I don't see any difference in qualifications between you two. In fact, Thorgrím owns a good farm and has much property as well as much support from kinsmen, whereas you have no farm and little property. Nor would I wish to insult Gizur by suggesting that he dispose of his daughter otherwise than he pleases; because I am much beholden to him." Arnór said: "Only then do I profit from having valuable kinsmen if they help me make a better match and if you support my suit.

You promise him your friendship, and then he will probably give me the girl; because then it will be thought an equal match, even if so fine a man as Thorgrím was rejected before."

Glúm allowed himself to be persuaded, and accompanied Arnór to Gizur, presenting the matter to him. Gizur answered: "Very possibly people will say, Glúm, that I make a mistake in giving my daughter to your kinsman Arnór whereas I did not see fit to give her to Thorgrím."

Glum said: "That is so; yet this is to be taken into account that you will, in return, gain my friendship if you will give a favorable answer to our suit."

Gizur answered: "That is indeed worth a great deal; yet I suspect that thereby I shall incur the hostility of others."

Glúm said: "Of course, you will have to decide that yourself; but it will make a great difference in my attitude toward you how you decide." Then Gizur said: "Neither shall you this time return without having achieved your purpose," and with that he extended his hand and allowed Arnór to betroth Thórdís to himself. Glúm added that he would make this contribution to the settlement that the marriage was to be that fall at Thverá. And with that they parted.

Now Arnór had malt lying in storage at Gásir, and he himself and a man-servant were to go and fetch it. As it happened, Thorgrím Thórisson that same day rode to the baths when Arnór and his servant were expected from the coast with the malt. Thorgrím and his six servants were at Hrafnagil, taking the baths, when Arnór and his man on their way from the coast were about to cross the river that flows through the Eyjafjörð Valley. Thorgrím said to his servants: "Wouldn't it be a good idea to fall upon Arnór and his servant? Let us not lose the malt, even if I must forego the bride."

And so Thorgrím and his men went toward them with drawn swords; but when Arnór saw how many were against him he drove his horse into the river and forded it, leaving the packhorses on the west bank.

Then Thorgrím said: "Luck is not against us in everything: it is we who'll drink, even though they dispose of the bride."

Thorgrím rode to his farm at South Espihól. At this time his father Thórir had lost his eyesight. The men with Thorgrím were in a merry mood and laughed a lot, so Thórir asked them what was so laughable. They said they did not know which party would celebrate the feast first. They told about the booty they had made and how they had driven off those who owned it—"and the bridegroom into the water."

When Thórir heard that he said: "Do you then consider your affairs in such good state, since you laugh so much, or how do you propose to get out of your difficulty? Do you mean to sleep here tonight and require no other provision? If so, you don't know what kind of man Glúm is, if you think he will be pleased with what happened to his kinsman. I hold it advisable to gather men, for in all likelihood Glúm has already collected many about him."

At that time there was a ford over the river where there is none now. During the night Thorgrím collected eighty fighting men and they made ready to defend themselves on the knoll facing the river, because the ford was near it.

Now to tell about Arnór: he came to Glúm and reported what had happened. Glúm said: "That is what I expected, that they would not let matters rest. But we face this quandary: either we shall suffer ignominy, if we don't do anything about it or, what is entirely unlikely, gain credit if we try to achieve redress. However, let us now collect men."

When daylight came Glúm approached the river with sixty men, intending to ride across it. But the Espihól people pelted them with rocks, so they could not cross. Glúm turned back, and they bombarded each other with rocks and missiles across the river. When the men of the district became aware of the fighting they hurried to the scene in the course of the day to intercede between them. The parties came to terms, and the Esphœlings were asked what restitution they were willing to make for the insult they had offered Arnór, and the reply came that no compensation would be forthcoming for Arnór's having deserted his sacks of malt. Then it was suggested that Glúm should use his influence to sue for Herthrúð, the other of Gizur's daughters, for Thorgrím, and that the marriage between Arnór and Thordís was to take place only on the condition that Glúm arranged to have Herthrúð marry Thorgrím; Thorgrím was considered the better match of the two. And as many exerted their influence in the matter Glúm promised his assistance.

He met with Gizur and broached the suit to him with these words: "It may seem presumptuous for me to try to arrange matters for both my kinsmen and you people of Espihól. But in order to avoid more mischief being done in our district I consider myself bound to show you my good will—if you do as I wish."

Gizur replied: "It appears advisable that you have your way as your proposal seems advantageous for my daughter."

And so arrangements were made for both weddings. Subsequently Arnór established himself at Uppsalir, and

Thorgrím dwelled at Möðrufell farm. Arnór had a son called Steinólf. Thorgrím also had a son. His name was Arngrím, and he gave promise during his youth of becoming a fine man.

Chapter 12

Saldís fostered the sons of both her daughters. Arngrím was two years older than Steinólf. There were at that time no two youths in the Eyjafjörð District better liked and more accomplished than they, and they were very fond of each other. One day, when Arngrím was six years old and Steinólf four, Steinólf asked Arngrím to lend him his brass toy horse,[29] and Arngrím answered: "I shall give it to you, because it is your plaything rather than mine, for you are younger." And Steinólf told his foster-mother what a fine present he had gotten. She said it was a good thing they got along so well.

A certain woman called Oddbjörg went about the district at that time, a cheerful person, wise and capable of seeing into the future. It was considered of great importance for housewives in the neighborhood to make her welcome, for she was likely to say something good or bad, according to how she was treated. When she came to Uppsalir Saldís made her welcome and asked her to predict something about the boys, preferably something good.

She said: "These boys do look promising, but whether their good luck will hold out, that is difficult for me to foretell."

Saldís said: "I believe you don't consider your entertainment here to have been so very good if you make such a disparaging remark."

Oddbjörg replied: "You don't need to think my words refer to the manner of your entertainment, and you don't need to be so sensitive."

Saldís retorted: "You should be chary of your words if you have any misgivings."

The other replied: "I haven't as yet said too much about this, but I don't think they will be on friendly terms very long."

Saldís said: "I should think I deserved better for my good entertainment of you, and you shall be driven away if you come with prophesies of evil."

Oddbjörg retorted: "Now I don't feel that I need to hold back if you go on like that for no reason; nor shall I ever cross your threshold again; but whether you like it or not: this I can tell you that they will become mortal enemies, and that one thing worse than the other will come from it in the district." And with that Oddbjörg is out of the saga.

Chapter 13

It so happened at the General Assembly[30] that men in groups, people from the North Quarter and the West Fjords, flocked to the place set apart for wrestling matches, and the men from the North Quarter were getting the worst of it. Már, the son of Glúm, headed them. A man approached the group; his name was Ingólf, the son of Thorvald who lived at Rangárvellir in the south of Iceland. Már said to him: "You look like a powerful man and one likely to be very strong. Do this for me and help me in the wrestling match." He answered: "That I shall do for your sake." He did so and brought down the first, and the second, and the third who opposed him, and so it went on. Then the men from the North Quarter took heart. Már said: "If you ever need a recommendation anywhere I shall give you my assistance. What are your plans now?" Ingólf answered: "I have not made any as yet, but I would like to go north and seek some employment."

Már said: "In that case I want you to come with me, and I shall get you a job." Ingólf owned some good studhorses. The stallion he called Snækoll. When the General

59

Assembly adjourned Ingólf betook himself north to Thverá and stayed there for a while.

One day Már asked Ingólf what plans he had made. "We need an overseer, one who is rather handy. Here is a sled which you shall mend, and if you can do it, you are a skillful smith."

Ingólf answered: "Most gladly would I stay here; but it has happened at times that people thought that mischief was caused on the home pastures by my horses."

Már said: "No account of that would be taken here."

Thereupon Ingólf repaired the sled, and Glúm came by and looked at his work.

"Well done," he said. "By the way, what are your plans?"

Ingólf replied: "I have not decided yet."

Glúm said: "I am lacking an overseer, are you perchance accustomed to that kind of work?"

Ingólf answered: "Little on farms as large as this one; but I would be happy to stay here with you."

"Why not," said Glúm, "I notice that you and Már get along well together."

When Már returned home Ingólf told him what had occurred.

Már said: "I shall be pleased if things turn out well; but if my father does not like something you do I shall tell you three times. But if you then don't mend your ways I shan't tell you again." Thereupon Ingólf took up the work as overseer, and Glúm was well pleased with him.

One day Glúm and his overseer went to the horse-fights, Ingólf riding a mare of his, with the stallion running alongside. There was good sport at the horse-fight. Kálf of Stokkahlaða was there, too. He was the owner of an old work horse which, however, overcame every other stallion.

Kálf said: "Why not pit him against that jewel of the Thverá people?"

Glúm replied: "It would be unfair to pit that stallion against your work horse."

Kálf retorted: "Very likely the reason you are unwilling is because there is no courage in him. Maybe, though, that there is some truth in the old adage that 'like beast, like master.'"

Glúm answered: "You know nothing about that; nor will I, on Ingólf's behalf, refuse that fight. But on the condition that they are not to be goaded longer than he is willing."

Kálf said: "It is hardly to be expected that anything is done against your wishes."

The horses were led forth, and they fought well, and everybody was of the opinion that Ingólf's stallion was the better fighter. Then Glúm desired that they be separated. Then they all rode home. Ingólf remained there that year, and Glúm was well satisfied with him.

A meeting was held by the Djúpadal River, and among those present were Glúm and Ingólf with his stallion. Kálf also was there with his stallion. He was a friend of the Esphœling people, and he proposed that now the stallions should fight to a finish. Glúm said that Ingólf should decide about that, but Ingólf declared that he was reluctant to have them so do, yet was unwilling to draw back. So the horses were led forth. Kálf lashed his stallion on, but Ingólf's horse did better in every bout. Then Kálf struck Ingólf's stallion on the ear with his stick so he was stunned, and made his own horse attack him. Then Glúm went up to them to separate them and to restore the balance. The end was that Kálf's horse gave ground. Then there was a great outcry of the people, and at their parting Kálf struck Ingólf with his stick. Then people intervened.

Glúm said: "Let's pay no attention to that, this is the way every horse-fight ends here."

Már said to Ingólf: "My father will see to it that you are not shamed by this blow."

Chapter 14

A certain man called Thorkel lived at Hamar. Ingólf was
accustomed to go there and meet with the farmer's
daughter, a handsome woman. Her father had ample
means though he was not a man of influence. Yet Ingólf
did not neglect the management of Glúm's estate, but
made fewer tools than before.

Már spoke to him one time, saying: "I have noticed
that my father is displeased at your leaving the farm so
often."

Ingólf gave him a good answer, yet things went on the
same way. Már spoke to him a second and a third time,
but to no avail.

One evening when Ingólf came home late and every
one had eaten his fill, Glúm said: "Now to have some
entertainment let us choose trusties [patrons] for our-
selves. I am going to choose first. I have three trusties.
One is my money bag, another, my battle axe, a third,
my storehouse."

Then one after another chose his.

Then Glúm said: "What is your choice, Ingólf?"

He answered: "Thorkel at Hamar."

Then Glúm jumped up, with sword in hand, and went up to him and said: "A fitting trusty you chose for yourself!"

All could see he was filled with wrath. He left the house, and Ingólf with him.

Then Glúm said to him: "Now you go to your trusty and tell him you have slain Hloðu-Kálf."

He answered: "Why should I tell a lie on myself?"

Glúm said: "You are to do as I tell you."

Both walked a few steps together. Then Glúm turned into the barn. There was a calf there, and he struck its head off with his sword, then handed the weapon all bloody to Ingólf and said: "Go south now across the river and say to Thorkel that you expect support only from him, showing him the bloody sword, so that the evidence is clear."

He did as he was told. He found Thorkel and told him what had occurred, that he had remembered the blow Kálf had dealt him and that he had killed him, "and I look to you for protection as you promised."

Thorkel replied: "You are a big fool to have killed such a noble fellow. Get out of here at once. I don't want you killed on my premises."

Ingólf went back home and met Glúm. He asked him: "Well, how did your trusty turn out?"

Ingólf answered: "Not well."

Glúm said: "Then try my trusty now," and went out to the storehouse and said: "You will be in a bad predicament if that Hloðu-Kálf is found slain."

The next day the news of the slaying of Hloðu-Kálf of Stokkahlaða was spread about. And now Thorkel reported that the man who had committed that crime had come to him and admitted it; and all believed that.

That winter wore on. Glúm sent Ingólf north to Einar Konálsson, providing him with nine hundred and eighty ells of homespun, and said to him: "You have had no pay from me, but with your thrifty habits you may put these wares to good profit. But as to the manslaughter you are charged with, I shall take care of that, so no harm will come to you. I repaid you thus for your self-willedness. And if you ever return to Iceland you may come to me again."

Ingólf said: "This would I ask of you, that you will not let any one else marry the woman."

"That I promise you." Ingólf's horses were left behind, but Einar Konálsson procured passage for him to go abroad.

Thorvald prepared a suit against Ingólf for the slaying of Kálf. It was brought at the Hegraness Assembly,[31] and it looked as if he would be condemned to outlawry. Glúm was there too, as well as some of Ingólf's kinsmen. They met with Glúm and asked for his assistance, declaring that they would contribute to pay damages for him.

Glúm answered them: "I shall see to it that this case is settled without penalties."

Then, when the court convened to sit in judgment and the defense was called, Glúm declared that the suit was invalid: "You have prepared the suit against a man who did not commit the deed: it was I who did."

Then he cited witnesses to testify that the suit was invalid: "Because even if Ingólf did kill a barn-calf I would not blame him for that. Now I shall offer a composition more in agreement with what the man was worth than with the overbearing of you Espihól people." Thereupon the assembly broke up.

Ingólf stayed abroad that winter, but then he liked it no longer overseas. He expended the money realized from selling his wares, buying things of value, especially wall-hangings of great worth. Glúm had given him a good cloak, and that he exchanged for one made of the precious cloth called "scarlet."

During the summer that Ingólf was abroad, a certain man named Thjóðólf returned to Iceland. His mother lived at Æsustaðir. He came to Hamar and there met Helga. One day Glúm had gone to Hólar, and as he rode down to Saurbær farm Thjóðólf met him.

Then Glúm said: "I don't fancy your visiting at Hamar. It is I who will see to it whom Helga will marry, and if you don't stop going to Hamar I shall challenge you to a duel." Thjóðólf said that he would not contend against Glúm and desisted from going to Hamar.

Chapter 15

Ingólf returned to Iceland and proceeded to Thverá, where Glúm made him welcome and offered him lodgings at his farm, which he accepted.

One day Ingólf said to Glúm: "Now I would like you to look over my wares."

He complied, and thought Ingólf had made good bargains.

Then Ingólf said: "You gave me merchandise with which to pay for my journey. Now I want to say that all this belongs to you."

Glúm replied: "You have only such goods as I don't care to have."

"But here are some hangings," said Ingólf, "which I bought for you, those you must accept, and here is a tunic."

Glúm replied: "I shall accept your gifts."

One day Glúm asked Ingólf whether he would like to stay with him.

He replied: "It is my intention never to part with you, if there is any chance of that. I want to give you my stud of horses."

Glúm said: "I shall accept the horses, and now let's go to see Thorkel of Hamar today."

And so they did. Thorkel made Glúm welcome.

Then Glúm said: "You have done wrong to Ingólf; but now you can make restitution for that by giving him your daughter in marriage. He is deserving of this, and I shall add some property. I have found him to be an excellent man. But if you don't agree to this you will be sorry later."

Thorkel did agree to this, and Ingólf thus obtained the girl. He became a good farmer, a person to be relied on.

Chapter 16[32]

Glúm had married his daughter Thorlaug to Víga-Skúta
of Lake Mývatn in the North.[33] But on account of their
mutual disagreement Glúm sanctioned her coming home
to Thverá, leaving her thus single. Glúm was greatly displeased at that. Later, Arnór Kerlingarnef asked for her
hand and married her. Some persons of distinction are
descended from them. From that time on there was much
hostility between Glúm and Skúta.

One summer a vagrant came to see Skúta and asked
to be taken in. Skúta asked him what his trouble was. He
said he had committed a manslaughter and so didn't
feel safe in his district.

Skúta said: "I have no obligation to you. For that matter, what kind of work do you propose to do to earn my
protection?"

He answered: "What would you like me to do?"

Skúta said: "You are to go on an errand to Víga-Glúm
and speak to him in this wise, that you would consider it
necessary to ask his aid in conducting your case. I suppose you will meet him on his way to the Assembly. He is

a man ready to give help when it is needed; and maybe he will tell you to meet him there. You are to say to him that you are hard pressed and that you would rather talk to him alone, and maybe he will offer some advice. You are to request him to meet you in Mjaðnárdal, which goes up from the houses at Thverá and in which stand his chalets; and that you would like to meet him on a day agreed on." This, the vagrant consented to do. And everything went according to Skúta's plans. Then he returned to Skúta and told him how matters went.

Skúta said then: "In that case you have carried out your errand well, and now stay with me."

Time passed, and when the day came on which Glúm had promised to meet the man sent to him, Skúta got ready to leave his farm, accompanied by thirty men. He rode south, then crossed the Vöðla Heath to the so-called Red Ledge, and there dismounted.

Then Skúta said: "Here we shall halt a while, but I shall ride along the slope to see whether anything turns up worth catching."

Looking up the valley he saw a man of large stature and clad in a green cloak, and recognized Glúm. Skúta dismounted. The cloak he wore was of two colors, black and white. He left his horse in a clearing in the woods, then went up to the chalet there. By that time Glúm had entered the chalet. Skúta had in his hand the sword called Fluga and a helmet on his head. He went up to the door of the chalet and knocked on the wall, then went to stand along the wall. Glúm came out, unarmed, but saw no one and turned sidewise along the chalet. Then Skúta managed to get between him and the chalet door. Glúm recognized Skúta and took to his heels toward the steep cliffs overhanging the creek. Skúta called out to him to wait, but Glúm retorted that would be fair if they were equally well armed, and retreated toward the gulch, with Skúta in pursuit. Glúm plunged down into the gorge, while Skúta tried to find a possible way down. He saw a cloak floating in the creek, rushed down, and pierced it with his sword.

Then he heard a voice from above: "Little glory gained, ruining people's clothes."

Skúta looked up and recognized Glúm. Glúm knew that right under the edge of the cliff from which he had leapt there was a grassy ledge.

Then Skúta said: "This you are bound to remember, Glúm, that now you ran away and didn't wait for Skúta."

Glúm replied: "True, but I could wish you wouldn't run a shorter distance before the sun sets this evening." Then Glúm spoke this verse:

> 3. At half an ounce[34] every
>   alder prize I, southward.
>   Widespread woods oft sheltered
>   wolves[35] from their pursuers.

They parted there for the time being. Glúm went home and reported what deceitful trick had been played on him. He gathered men, declaring he would like to repay Skúta quickly. Within a short time he got sixty men together, and with them rode up the valley.

Skúta had mounted his horse when they parted, and rode along the slope. Then he saw the party of men on horseback and concluded it would not do for him to meet them. So he devised a plan. He broke the point of his spear from the shaft and used it as a staff, took the saddle off his horse, and rode bareback, turned his cloak inside out, and hallooed loudly.[36] They went after him and asked whether he had seen a man ride along the ridge, one armed and of imposing appearance. He said he had.

71

They asked: "And what is your name?"

He answered: "My name is Many in the Mývatn District, and Few in the Fiskilœkjar District."

They said: "You mean to answer us with taunts and mockery."

He declared he couldn't tell them anything more truthful, and so they parted. But as soon as they were gone he took up his weapons and saddle gear, and rode speedily to join his own men.

The party that had encountered Skúta found Glúm and told him they had met a man who answered them only with jibes, and also, what he called himself.

"You have shown little presence of mind," said Glúm. "That was Skúta whom you encountered; for what more true could he say than that in the Mývatn District there are many caves,[37] but in the Fiskilœkjar District there aren't any. And we were close to one another then. But let us ride after him anyway."

They rode till they came to the Ledges, and there Skúta's men were in front of them, where there was a narrow path easier to defend with thirty men than to attack with sixty.

Then Skúta said: "You are taking great pains to pursue me. Maybe you think you must avenge yourself for having had to flee. You showed great daring to leap into that gorge, and you weren't slow of foot on that occasion."

Glúm replied: "That is true; but you too learned the meaning of fear when you pretended to be the shepherd of the Eyjafjörð people, concealing your weapons and breaking some. And I believe you did not run a shorter distance than I did."

Skúta said: "However things have gone between us, so far, now you have the chance to attack us with a force twice as large as mine." Glúm replied: "I think we shall part for the time being, whatever people may think about it." Thereupon Skúta rode north, and Glúm, home to Thverá.

Chapter 17

When Thórir died, Thórarin set up house north of Espihól and lived there. Glúm had children with his wife.
Már was the name of one son, as was mentioned before,
another was called Vigfús. Both were promising but
altogether different in disposition, Már being taciturn
and gentle, whereas Vigfús was of a very boisterous disposition, unscrupulous, very strong, and dauntless.

A man lived with Glúm called Hallvarð. He had been
released from bondage by Glúm and was the fosterfather
of Vigfús. He had made much money and was tricky in
business matters. He entrusted his property to Vigfús.
He did not enjoy a good reputation. He had erected a
storehouse at the farm which is called "at Tjorn," up in
Eyjafjarðardal, and his popularity was not increased thereby, because when it came to driving home the sheep from
the common pasture he would often appropriate one
that didn't belong to him. But Vigfús was a great merchant.

A certain man lived at the farm of Jórunnarstaðir who
was called Halli and nicknamed the White. He was the

74

son of Thorbjörn. His mother's name was Vigdís, a daughter of Auðun rotin. Halli had fostered Einar Eyjólfsson and thus had come to live at Saurbær. Halli, who was blind, had to do with all cases in the district calling for reconciliation, for he was both wise and just in delivering judgment. He had three sons, Orm, and Brúsi the Skald, both of whom lived at the Torfufell farm, and Bárð, who lived at Skaldsstaðir. He was a boisterous and unscrupulous man, rash of speech and abusive. He was married to Una, the daughter of Oddkel of Thjórsárdal.

One fall there disappeared ten or twelve wethers of Halli's from the common pasture, nor could they be located. And when Bárð and his father Halli met, the latter asked what he believed had become of these wethers.

Bárð answered: "I am not surprised that some sheep disappear, seeing that thieves live in the house nearest to us since Hallvarð moved into this neighborhood."

Halli said: "I would like you to prepare a suit against him, summoning him for theft; and I believe that Glúm won't be able to acquit him of the verdict of the 'twelve'[38] if I prepare a charge of theft against Hallvarð." Bárð replied: "It might be difficult for you to press for a verdict of the 'twelve' against Glúm and his son."

Chapter 18

So Bárð prepared his suit. When Vigfús got to know that, he told his father Glúm that he would be greatly displeased if a charge of theft were preferred against his fosterfather.

Glúm answered: "You know that Hallvarð is untrustworthy, and it might cause animosity to acquit him of the charge."

Vigfús said: "I could wish that we were dealing with more important matters than the theft of a few sheep."

Glúm replied: "To me it would seem better to pay damages for him—and let him transfer his belongings to my farm for ought I care—rather than risk my standing for such a person."

Now people flocked to the Assembly, and the case was brought up before the court, and Glúm was to deliver the verdict of the jury. Then Vigfús became aware that Glúm was going to pronounce Hallvarð guilty, so he went before the court and declared that if his fosterfather were judged guilty it would be his wish that Glúm would have reason to consider that verdict dearly bought. The outcome was, in fact, that Glúm quashed the suit, thus acquitting Hallvarð. And that caused Glúm to lose much respect in the district.

When a winter or two had passed Halli missed a boar fed in the home pasture, one so fat that he could hardly get up. Bárð came there one day and asked whether the boar had been slaughtered. Halli replied that he had disappeared. Bárð said: "He probably has gone to look for the sheep that were stolen last fall." Halli replied: "I suppose they have all gone the same way. Would you care to summon Hallvarð for theft?" Bárð answered: "That I shall do, for now Glúm won't succeed in getting him acquitted; because it was Vigfús who was instrumental in getting him acquitted, but now he isn't in the country." Bárð assumed the conduct of the case and went to serve the summons on Hallvarð. And when he found him he effected a quick conclusion to the suit by striking off his head. Then he told his father what he had done. Halli strongly disapproved of the deed and immediately went to Glúm, offering to let him be sole arbiter. Glúm accepted that, adjudging himself small damages, but had them pay for the boar and the sheep. That decision won him much approbation. But when Vigfús returned to Iceland he was incensed at the slaying of Hallvarð.

Glúm said to him: "It will not do to break the agreement we have reached." And though they met occasionally, Bárð and Vigfús did not pick a quarrel.

The following summer a horse-fight was arranged in which all stallions in the district were to be goaded to fight, in such fashion that those of the upper part of the district were to be pitted against those of the lower part; and one man from either part was to be selected to decide which horse came out the winner, and their decisions were to stand. For the upper part, Bárð was chosen for that, and for the lower, Vigfús, the son of Glúm. There were a good many horses, it was good sport, and there were many draws. Many horse-fights took place at the same time during the day. The outcome was that an equal number had put up a good fight and had turned tail; and all agreed that it was a draw.

At that time Vigfús stated that he had a stallion which had not been in the contest, "and he is the best among those brought here today. Lead any other of the stallions against him."

Bárð answered: "This horse looks vicious to us; and we shan't lead any horse against him, and yet maintain that it was a draw."

Vigfús said: "In that case you have no match for him in your district. You surely don't want people to say that you have no match for us."

Bárð replied: "You, Vigfús, have been fair in your decisions so far; but now I'm not so sure. One can see now that you probably more often stood near the pantry shelves and helped your mother decide about the cooking than attended horse-fights; and the color of your beard points that way, too."[39]

Vigfús and many others laughed about that remark.

One of Halli's servants returned home from the horse-fight and was asked how it had turned out.

The servant replied: "They were considered matched."

Halli then asked: "Did Bárð and Vigfús come to terms?"

The servant answered: "Certainly, yet Bárð said something to Vigfús."

Halli asked: "And what was that?"

The servant repeated what was said.

Halli said: "Evil will come of that."

The servant said: "But Vigfús laughed about it."

Halli answered: "It is the habit of Glúm and his sons to laugh when the murderous mood is upon them."

The two, Halli and Bárð, met; and Halli asked his son what had come upon him to say something so hideous, "and I fear this will lead to much misfortune. The only way out will be for you to leave the country and procure timber for building.[40] And stay abroad for three years. Else you are doomed to death."

Bárð said: "All this wouldn't matter so much if you weren't such a coward. That's what old age does to you, that you fear for your sons."

Halli replied: "Even though you are dauntless it would be difficult for you to maintain yourself in the district."

Bárð heeded his father's advice and left the country. Then Halli paid a vagrant to go to the Skagafjörð District and to the districts west of it and tell people that the reason Bárð had left the country and didn't dare to do otherwise was because of Glúm and his sons, on account of a word or two. "And no one dares to counter them in the district."

He did as Halli bade him. This ruse was hit upon so that Bárð's kin could sit in peace on his account. Bárð stayed abroad for one year, then returned to his farm.

Chapter 19

Halli had taken care of Bárð's farm while he was abroad,
and had timber cut in the forest in Mjaðmárdal which belonged to Bárð. Bárð himself had brought along big
logs to Iceland. He lived sometimes on his own farm and
sometimes with his father. Bárð told his father that he
intended to fetch his timber.

Halli said: "I should want you not to convey it yourself, for Glúm and his sons can't be trusted."

Bárð replied that people were not likely to be aware
of their movements. He and one servant went to convey
the timber, and they had a large number of horses along.
Una, his wife, had gone to Víðiness to visit her sister
Oddkatla and Bárð went there too. Hlenni offered to
have another servant accompany him to the woods whilst
he himself waited for them at his place, because he considered that a wise precaution. But Bárð said he didn't
need him.

The two sisters saw him on his way. But as they were
returning, Una looked over her shoulder after Bárð and

80

fell in a faint; and when she came to her senses her sister asked her what she had seen.

She said: "I saw dead men go up to Bárð. He is likely to be fey,[41] and I shall probably never see him again."

Bárð and the servant went on their way, and mist drifted over the forest as they entered it. They lashed the timber together and hobbled their horses.

Early in the morning a shepherd from Thverá was abroad. It often happened that Vigfús met with shepherds to ask for news, and so he did that morning.

He said: "It is remarkable how you can locate sheep in such a fog. I should never be able to find the sheep in such a fog."

The shepherd answered: "I had little trouble finding the sheep. But the men I saw in the forest this morning had more trouble locating their horses, though they stood near by them. Yet they were in high spirits. One of them wore a green tunic and had a shield at his side."

Vigfús asked whether he had recognized the man.

The shepherd said he thought it was Bárð, "because he owns the forest they were in."

Vigfús said: "Go fetch three of my horses."

Two Norwegians were staying at Thverá. Vigfús requested them to come with him, saying that he was going to ride to the baths. When leaving the farm he turned south, past Laugardal.[42]

Then the Norwegians asked: "In which direction are you going now?"

He answered: "First on my errands," as he rode far ahead of them. They rode in a southerly direction on the height above the farms until they saw Bárð coming out of the woods, with his horses dragging the timber.

Bárð's servant perceived the men riding after them and said: "These men are pursuing us fast."

81

"Of what concern is that to us?" asked Bárð.

The man servant answered: "It is Vigfús who is pursuing us, and I would like to avoid them; and no ignominy will attach to that so long as we don't know what their intentions are."

Bárð replied: "Vigfús will hardly attack me, he with two others, if you are not with me."

The servant said: "I would prefer to go on with the horses and that you ride to Víðiness. It won't be regarded as dishonorable if you go there since you have business there. And actually you don't know for sure the reason for their riding after us. But Hlenni said you should not trust them."

Bárð said: "You shall ride ahead and forewarn people if I stay out longer than expected; because matters won't be so quickly settled between Vigfús and me if we are going to fight it out together. But he is too chivalrous a man to attack me with two others. But if there are two of us against three of them they are likely to enjoy their advantage in numbers."

The man did as Bárð told him, and Bárð unfastened his shield and got himself ready the best he could. When they met, Bárð asked what business they had in hand. Vigfús replied that both of them would not escape alive from their meeting. Bárð said he was prepared for them both to contend against each other, "but it does not show valor for three to attack one."

Then the two Norwegians declared they would have remained behind if they had known the nature of Vigfús's business, and that they would not assist him unless men came to aid Bárð, seeing that his companion had fled. Vigfús bade them see first how things would turn out. Thereupon Bárð and Vigfús fought together for a long time, with neither suffering a wound. But it looked less

82

hopeful for Vigfús, for he was forced to retreat every time before he could get into a position for a lunge. Bárð defended himself excellently with his sword and received no wounds. To the Norwegians it seemed a big disgrace if Vigfús were slain, with them standing by and if men came to aid Bárð. So they fell upon him and slew him. He was dead when Hlenni and his men arrived.

Vigfús and his companions rode home. Glúm was disconcerted by their deed and declared that by it the troubles in the district would be greatly increased. Halli looked up his fosterson Einar in Saurbær and requested him to take charge of the suit after Bárð. It devolved upon him, he said, to prosecute the case for his kinsman and fosterbrother. Then both went to see Thórarin and ask for his support. Thórarin declared he could not think of any one he would rather have dealings with than Halli and they cemented their friendship with oaths, to stand together both in this case and every other.

The suits were brought before the Assembly, and terms for a settlement were sought. However, there was so much opposition that there was no chance of it, because intrepid men, both from Möðruvellir and from Espihól, men skilled in the laws, stood out against it. The case ended with the two Norwegians being outlawed; and as to Vigfús, money was given him so he could procure passage abroad. He was to have three summers' time for trying to procure passage and meanwhile to have three places of residence every year. Which is to say, he was sentenced to "the lesser outlawry." He was not allowed to stay at home at Thverá because of the holiness of the place. He dwelled a long time at Uppsalir while people thought he was in other parts of the country; nor did he want to leave at the set time, and thus he incurred full outlawry. Glúm secretly gave him shelter. But by rights men condemned to outlawry were not to be there, for Frey, to whom the temple there was dedicated, had forbidden it. This went on for six years.

Chapter 20

Now we take up the story where the two fosterbrothers, Arngrím and Steinólf, were growing up together. When Thórir of Möðruvellir died, Arngrím betook himself to his father's farm, together with Steinólf, and there was as much affection between them as there had ever been. Arngrím married. His wife was Thordís, the daughter of Björn. She was the sister of Arnór Kerlingarnef. Steinólf engaged in trading voyages, staying with Arngrím whenever he was in Iceland. One summer, when Steinólf arrived in the Eyjafjörð District Arngrím did not invite him to stay with him; nor did he speak with him when they met, and gave as a reason that he (Steinólf) had talked more with Thordís, his wife, than was proper.[43] But most people thereabouts were of the opinion that there was little or no ground for his suspicion. Then Glúm invited Steinólf to stay with him, and for some years he did live with him, whenever he was in the country, and their relations as kinsmen were cordial. Steinólf was a man of many skills. But one summer Glúm did not invite him to live with him, saying that he preferred him to stay with his father (Arnór) at Uppsalir.

"And the reason why I do not invite you to stay with me is that your visits in the neighborhood don't seem safe to me. But if you stay with your father you are free to come here to Thverá, and you will always be welcome."

So it went on in this fashion for several years, the years when Vigfús was at Uppsalir with Arnór Redcheek in hiding as an outlaw. Steinólf, as said, was also there.

One fall, a certain farmer at Öxnafell married off his daughter and invited to the marriage feast all the farmers of greatest consequence in the Eyjafjörð District, among them also Eyjólf. He came to Thverá, intending to go to the feast together with Glúm. But Glúm said he himself would not go. Steinólf said: "It seems to me you will be going back on your word in not attending, after having accepted the invitation." Glúm replied: "Less harm will result from my going back on my word than from your unwariness; and I will not go. A great undertaking for one farmer to invite so many men of influence—if there is no trickery in it! For I have a suspicion of what is at the bottom of this party. This farmer is not undertaking this on his own initiative; and it would be my advice that my friends do not go."

Steinólf went to the banquet, as did the others who had been invited; but not Glúm. While there, Einar Eyjólfsson, Thorvald, and Arngrím talked much together. On the day men were about to leave, Einar spoke at length about the administration of the district. He made the point that it was always proper, when many had gathered, to discuss what at the time seemed most needful, and that then things would be much better: "for a long time there has been hostility between ambitious men here. I am particularly referring to the kinsmen Arngrím and Steinólf. There has been ill feeling between them;

but I am of the opinion that slander and the talk of enemies have caused that. Now Arngrím wishes to invite Steinólf to his home and entertain him well, if Steinólf wants to accept that; and I could wish that you two come to an understanding." Steinólf said that he would gladly do that, and declared he knew of nothing he had done to Arngrím and that he was fonder of him than of any other man. Thereupon all present departed to their homes. Steinólf went with Arngrím and stayed with him for several days and was very well entertained.

Chapter 21

One day Arngrím asked Steinólf whether he cared to
go with him down to Grund farm to take part in the
drinking bout there, and to stay there two or three nights.
He answered: "I shall prefer to stay here while you are
gone, and go another time when you stay home." Arngrím said it was allright for him to stay there if he did
not care to go with him. Thereupon Arngrím betook himself to Grund, leaving Steinólf behind at Möörufell for
the night. Next morning Steinólf sat by the fire, busy
with some handiwork. That was a small box which belonged to the lady of the house. At that moment Arngrím
came in, together with Thorvald Barb. And as they
entered the living room where the fire burned Steinólf
was bending down over his work. Then Arngrím struck
him on the head with his axe so he fell dead immediately.
At that moment the lady of the house walked past him
and said: "Strike, you wretch. That was the design of
men more cunning than you; and from this day I shall
never be your wife." Thereupon she betook herself back

to Arnór Kerlingarnef and never after got into the same bed with Arngrím. Before she left the house she said: "That will be your punishment, Arngrím, that you will have few days to live, and those that you do live will be the worse for you." Later on she married Ásgrím Elliða-Grímsson.

Arngrím and his father Thorgrím rode to Espihól and told Thórarin what had happened and asked for his help, saying that they had neither the wits nor the popular support to oppose Glúm, but that Thórarin was both shrewd and popular. He answered, saying that this deed looked bad to him and that he feared evil would result from it. Thorvald was of the opinion that it wasn't any use to blame one's self for the deed and said he thought that he, Thórarin, was likely soon to have to deal with yet greater difficulties unless he lent them his support; and both declared that it might very well be that they would get supporters if only he spoke for them. To this, Thórarin answered: "My advice is that both of you transfer your residence to this place, from Grund and from Möðrufell, and that we collect men as fast as possible and lay our properties together before Glúm becomes aware of it." And they did so, before Glúm learned of it. And when he did, he gathered men and proceeded against them at once. But he was not successful in attacking them, because the Esphœling people were more numerous.

Both parties lay quiet during the winter, nor did they ever manage to overcome Glúm that winter. He was so much on his guard that he never was found in the bed that was made for him. Nights he often slept little, with himself and Már discussing their litigation. One night Már asked him how he had slept. Then Glúm spoke this verse:

4. Sleep I shall not sweetly,
   sword-wielder, in this house—nor
   will the men-of-wealth[44] e'er
   wish to make good my lost friend—
   before my wand-of-wounds[45] I
   wield anew against them:
   lifted I have it for little,
   or lesser, cause quite often.

"And now I shall tell you my dream: I thought I was walking outside my farm, alone and unarmed, and I thought I saw Thórarin walk toward me, with a big whetstone in his hand, and I seemed ill prepared for our encounter. And when I considered the situation I beheld another whetstone at my side, and I went to meet him. And when we met, each was about to strike the other, and the stones clashed, and there was a loud crash." Már asked: "Did it seem to you a crash heard throughout the house?" Glúm replied: "It was louder than that." "Then could it be called a crash heard throughout the district?" Glúm answered: "That was more like it, for I thought I was sure it was heard throughout the whole district. And when I awoke I spoke this verse:

5. The hardy sea-stag-steerer[46]
   struck me with a whetstone—
   in my sleep I saw this—
   sending it against me;
   but in my sleep meseemed I
   seized another whetstone,
   hurling it at the hapless
   hero, with seething rage filled."

Már said it was likely that the old saying would prove true, "that each of you struck the other with an evil stone before things came to a standstill."[47] Glúm answered: "Not unlikely that this will come to pass, for I have many forebodings. I must tell you another dream: I thought I stood outside when I saw two women.[48] They carried a trough between them, and they stopped on the field called Hrísateig[49] and poured blood over the whole district. Then I awoke, and I consider this must portend events of importance, and I spoke a verse:

> 6. Saw the gold-ring-giver[50]
> groups of godheads riding
> aloft o'er the land—clash of
> lances heard I, and arms-din,
> where, battle-eager, o'er bloody
> bodies Valkyries poured forth
> dew-of-wounds[51]—was then
> Viðrir[52] much pleased thereby."

That morning Már went to Möðrufell with seventeen men in order to summon Arngrím for the slaying, while Glúm remained at home with five men and requested the others to return quickly. Jöður, a follower of Glúm, stayed at the farm, as did Eyjólf, a son of Thorleif the Tall, Thorvald Tasaldi, the son of Glúm's sister, and two thralls.

91

Chapter 22

Helga, Glúm's sister, who had been married to Steingrím
at Sigluvík, had come to Laugaland at that time. She was
the mother of Thorvald Tasaldi, who then was eighteen
years old. Thorvarð Örnólfsson was the name of a certain
man. He was the son of Yngvild, nicknamed Everyone's
Sister.[53] He lived at Kristness. Guðbrand was the name of
his twelve-year-old son. Thorvarð was a shrewd man, old
at that time, and not altogether well-intentioned. He
was up and about early that morning and told his boy
to lead out the horses, and then they rode to Thverá.
When they arrived there Már had just left. Glúm made
Thorvarð welcome. He asked whether terms had been
sought between the two parties. Glúm said they had not.
Thorvarð asked: "Has any action been brought?" Glúm
said no. "A day like this would be very suitable for that
purpose," said Thorvarð. "There is a thick fog, and no
one will become aware of it if we proceed quietly."[54]
Thereupon Glúm informed him how matters stood there
at Thverá, that only six men were left at home. Thorvarð replied: "You have rather few people with you. Yet
your plan is likely to succeed."

Thereupon Thorvarð rode to Espihól and found that the people there had not yet got up when he arrived. He met Thórarin and asked: "What plan of procedure do you propose to follow? Are you prepared to offer Glúm some terms for this case of manslaughter?" Thórarin answered: "It seems to us difficult to offer Glúm any terms." Thorvarð asked: "Has any suit for manslaughter been instituted?" Thórarin answered: "Not so far as I have learned, or have you?" Thorvarð replied: "This morning Már went with seventeen men to open the case, leaving Glúm with five others behind, so that there would be an excellent opportunity for you to obtain redress.[55] But the reason you have so little success is that you make no quick decisions like Glúm." Thórarin replied: "I don't care to enter trivial counterclaims." Thorvarð said: "You ought to consider whether there were any causes to lead to the slaying of Steinólf. Didn't he seduce Arngrím's wife? I certainly think that such a matter will not be considered trivial." Thórarin replied: "I don't like to enter such a charge." Thorvarð said: "Of what use is it to talk that way? Didn't it serve Glúm to outlaw Sigmund, your kinsman by marriage, when he slew him? And now the most important thing is not to be humbled." Thórarin said: "I don't know but that is the thing to do."

Then they arose, and Thorvald Barb urged them to ride to Uppsalir and summons Steinólf on a charge involving outlawry.[56] Thórarin observed: "That is hardly advisable, and yet that is what we shall do." They were fifteen altogether, of whom seven are known by name, to wit, Thórarin and Thorvald Barb, Ketil, his son, Arngrím, Eystein Berserk, Thórð Hrafnsson who lived at Stokkahlaða and was the husband of Vigdís, the daughter of Thórir, who before had been married to Sigmund, and finally Eyvind the Norwegian. He was staying with

93

Thórð. They all betook themselves to Uppsalir, but Thorvarð went to Öngulsstaðir. There dwelled a worthy farmer, Halli the Stout. But his own son (Guðmund) he sent to Thverá, bidding him to tell Glúm of the intention of the Espihól people, "and then hasten to meet me."

When Thorvarð arrived at Öngulsstaðir, Halli asked him what news he had to tell. "Nothing, as yet," he replied. Later on he told Halli how matters stood. Halli thought he saw how Thorvarð probably had started all this, and declared that men like him were causing much mischief and that he meant to set everybody at loggerheads. "And it would be a good thing if you were killed." Halli proceeded quickly, with everybody at his disposal, both men and women, meaning to go between the parties if required.

Guðbrand (Thorvarð's son) arrived at Thverá and informed Glúm that this father had sent him to tell him what had occurred, "and he was under obligation to tell you what should be of concern to you, that the people of Espihól intend to summon Steinólf on the charge of outlawry." Thereupon Glúm said: "Why didn't your father come himself?" Guðbrand answered: "Isn't it all the same who of us brought you the message?" Glúm said: "Your father acted wisely when he sent you here, in case we needed men," and he lifted the boy down and hobbled his horse. Then Guðbrand said: "My father told me to hasten home." Glúm replied: "Not so; rather does your father wish that you show your bravery today."

Meanwhile Thorvarð said: "Long does my son Guðbrand tarry." Halli said: "Where did he go?" Thorvarð answered: "I sent him to Thverá." Halli replied: "Good that you have encountered other men as crafty as you; that is as it should be."

The men from Espihól rode across the river. Glúm saw

that they intended to do so at the Knarrarvað ford.[57] Then he said that Már was rather too slow in coming. Thereupon he ran out of the farm yard and after them, as did those who were with him, six men, including Guð-brand. Glúm had his shield along and his halberd. He was girt with his sword and ran onto the path ahead of them, with his men after him. When Thórarin saw him coming he told his men to ride on their way, and neither faster nor slower, "and no one will blame us for that." Thórð Hrafnsson asked him whether they, with twenty men, were going to let themselves be chased by Glúm with six. Thórarin answered: "Let us ride on, because Glúm means to delay us and thus wait for other men of his to join him." Thórð said: "It is not strange that we so often are worsted by Glúm when you are equally matched, since you don't dare to stand up to him when he has inferior numbers; and he is not going to chase me," and he got off his horse. Eystein Berserk said that he was not going to ride away "and they would then maintain that they had chased us." Thórarin said: "That does not seem advisable."

When Glúm saw that they were not moving on he slowed up, too, and addressed Thórarin and asked him what they had in mind in riding to Uppsalir. Thórarin replied that they had summoned Steinólf for deeds entailing outlawry. Then said Glúm: "Aren't you pursuing this matter too hastily, shouldn't an offer to come to terms precede it, so that we might discuss the case a bit, and so that this matter might be settled?" Thórarin perceived that Glúm wanted to delay them, and told his men to ride on; and so they did. Glúm asked: "Why don't you wait?"

But they rode on, and the slower they went, the slower Glúm went, waiting for his men. He said: "This case won't have much popular support if you bring up false accusations, and it will turn out a discomfiture for you." "Things won't go that way, this time," said Thórarin, "but it is difficult to deal with you."

Glúm managed to ride ahead of them as they rode along, talking with them and thus delaying them. But when he saw that he could not retard them and knew that he could expect his own men, he hurled his spear at Arngrím. It went through both the saddle bows and his thigh, so that Arngrím was little able to fight that day. Thereupon Eystein was the first to rush at Glúm, and Thorvald Tasaldi in his turn against him, and both fought together; and those who were farthest away from their encounter considered themselves fortunate, for both were dauntless men of great strength. Each dealt the other many and great blows. Thorvald assailed Glúm vigorously, and many with him, but he together with his men retreated, defending themselves. But Thórarin did not get off his horse, thinking there were plenty against one already.

Chapter 23

A man came running, as they were fighting. He was dressed in a leather cloak and wielded a sword. He arrived at the moment when Thorvald Tasaldi was felled by Eystein, and at once rushed at Eystein and dealt him a mortal blow. Then he joined Glúm, whereupon the latter said this: "Welcome, Thundarbenda![58] I made a good purchase when I bought you. You are likely to repay your purchase price today." Now Glúm owned a thrall by that name—for which reason he spoke thus—; but actually it was his son Vigfús; however, few knew him, or rather, no one except Glúm, because he had been three years in outlawry and in hiding—most people thought he had gone abroad.

It so happened that Glúm, as he was retreating, fell and lay on the ground, and two of his thralls covered him with their bodies, and were killed by spear thrusts. At that moment Már arrived with his men. Then Thórarin got off his horse, and the two fought, without any one else taking part in their fight. But Glúm regained his feet and fought then like a man. Now there was no difference in numbers between them.

Eirík was the name of one of Thórarin's servants. He was busy with his work that morning. He had neither shield nor weapon, but he got him a club and went to the assistance of Thórarin, and Glúm had the greatest trouble warding him off, because both shields and men suffered damage from the cudgel he fought with.

We are told that Halldóra, Glúm's wife, summoned women to go with her, saying: "We shall bandage the wounds of the men in whom there is still life, to whichever side they belong." And as she was approaching the place where the fight was Thórarin was felled by Már, with his shoulder severed, so that his lungs protruded through the wound. Halldóra bandaged him and tended him till the battle came to an end.

Halli the Stout was the first to intervene between them, he and many others. The battle ended with five of the Espihól people having fallen, namely: Thorvald Barb, Arngrím, Eystein, Eirík, and Eyvind the Norwegian. On Glúm's side Thorvald Tasaldi had fallen; also Eyólf Thorleifsson, Jöður, and two thralls.

Thórarin proceeded home with his companions, as Glúm did with his men. He had the dead transported into a shed. Thorvald Barb was laid out most honorably, in that cloths were laid under him and he was sewed up in a hide. When Glúm and his men had come home he said to Halldóra: "Our undertaking today would probably have turned out favorably if you had stayed home. Then Thórarin would not have escaped alive." She replied that there was little chance for Thórarin to live, "but even if he survives you would not be able to stay in the district but for a short time; but if he dies you will never be permitted to live in our country."

Later on Glúm said to Guðbrand: "You won great renown today when you felled Thorvald, and you have been of great help to us today." Guðbrand answered, saying that it had not been that way, that he had only defended himself. Glúm said: "I saw plainly what happened, for one only a child to have felled such a strong fighter as Thorvald Barb, and you will become famous for that deed. It was for just such a deed that I won distinction in foreign parts when I slew the berserker." Guðbrand replied: "I did not slay Thorvald." Glúm said: "It is not to be denied, my friend, that you gave him the deathblow. Don't shrink from being so fortunate!" And he argued this with Guðbrand till he believed and admitted it, thinking it to be an honor; nor could he deny it any longer that it was true. And so later on he was declared to have been Thorvald's slayer. And that appeared of lesser advantage than they thought for those who chose the death of Thorvald as foundation for the prosecution.

It is said that Glúm remarked: "I am displeased that Már is having that mere scratch on his head bandaged." That is what he called the place where Már had received a crosswise split on the head. Már replied: "I would require that even less if I had lain down and had my thralls shield me." Then Glúm said: "Hard to mow was Hrísateig Field today, boys." Már said: "For you it will prove to have been hard to mow, because now you are likely to have the Thverá fields harvested out of your hands." Glúm replied: "I consider that you can't be so sure of that." Már said: "Maybe that I don't know for sure; events will prove though that I am right."

When Helga, Glúm's sister, learned about the battle she came to Thverá and asked how her son Thorvald Tasaldi had borne himself. Glúm replied: "There never was a braver man." Then she said: "I would rather have him dead if so it had to be." She asked for permission to take the youth home with her[59] and that was granted her, and she had him lifted on to a sled and tended gently, and when she arrived at home with him she cleaned his wounds, then bandaged them; and his condition improved so that he could talk to people.

According to the law at that time if equally many men fell on either side in a battle it was to be regarded as a draw, even though it was thought there was a difference in rank between them; but the party suffering the greater loss of life was to select one of their dead for whose death a suit was to be preferred. And though something might happen in the pursuit of the case so that it might seem better to have chosen some one else, no change was allowed. Now when Thórarin learned that Thorvald Tasaldi was still alive, he chose Thorvald Barb, his own brother, to enter a suit for. But a little later he heard that his death was attributed to Guðbrand, and then he wished he had chosen some one else; but now he had to go on with whom he had chosen before.

Now when they met Einar Eyjólfsson, Thórarin said that now he would take up the suit they had agreed upon. He said: "I have the same thing in mind as when Bárð was slain." Then Einar in summer took up the conduct of the case and prosecuted Glúm.

Thórarin lay wounded all summer, as did Thorvald Tasaldi, but both ultimately recovered. Glúm had a host of supporters at the Assembly, and so did the other side. Distinguished kinsmen on either side sought terms of conciliation. An agreement was reached whereby the death of Steinólf was to be compensated by Vigfús, the son of Glúm, being declared free from outlawry. But Guðbrand was declared guilty of the death of Thorvald. Glúm procured passage abroad for him. Both parties thereupon departed for home. Thorvarð and Thórarin were ill pleased with the outcome of their suit, Thórarin considering that he was awarded no compensation for the slaying of his brother Thorvald.

Glúm now was highly regarded. In the winter following, a verse became known which Glúm had lately composed:

> 7. Asks the winsome wine-cup-
> warder[60] what my deeds were.
> Of murderous battle, men are
> mindful no longer, woman.
> Slain lie, by the swordsmen
> sent to Hel, full many.
> — — — — — — — — — — — —
> — — — — — — — — — — — —

Chapter 24

One day, when people were taking the baths at the Hrafnagil hot springs, Thorvarð joined them. He was a very cheery man who amused himself with many things. He said: "Who is here who might entertain us with new stories?" The others replied: "It is you on whom we depend for all our fun and entertainment." He replied: "I don't think there is any better entertainment than to recite Glúm's verses; but I wonder why he considers that he has counted wrong in one verse where he tells about his manslaughters. What are we to think which that might be—for that matter which is more likely, that Guðbrand slew Thorvald or that Glúm did?" To many the latter seemed more likely.

Thorvarð now rode to see Thórarin and said: "I have been thinking of something: it seems to me we don't know the truth about the death of Thorvald Barb; because it is found in Glúm's verses that he thinks he had made a mistake in counting the number of his slayings." Thórarin replied: "I can hardly open the case again, even though this were true. Let matters rest now." "That is not advisable," said Thorvarð; "yet peace might prevail if matters had not been probed into. But now I shall make the truth known, and then this is likely to result in a greater disgrace for you Espihól people than ever before." Thórarin answered: "It will prove difficult, it seems to me, to take the case to the General Assembly, what with the support Glúm will have from his kinsmen." Thorvarð said: "I know a way out: summon him before the Hegraness Assembly.[61] There you will have the support of kinsmen, and it will be difficult for Glúm to make a defense there." Thórarin answered: "That advice I shall follow." Thereupon they parted.

A bad spring followed, and it was difficult to procure anything. Nevertheless Thórarin prepared a suit to be brought at that time against Glúm at the Hegraness Assembly, because all chieftains taking part in this assembly were bound by affinity to himself; but the horses could hardly make it over the highlands on account of the deep snow. Glúm resorted to entrusting a large cargo boat filled with weapons and provisions to his brother Thorstein. He was to steer in a westerly direction and arrive with them at the Assembly. But when they passed the mouth of the Úlfsdal they wrecked their ship and lost everything, both men and goods.

Glúm came to the Assembly with a hundred men and did not succeed in pitching his tents closer than outside the Assembly grounds. Einar Eyjólfsson had already arrived there, accompanied by the men of the Esphœling people.

Word was sent to Glúm to come forward and proceed with his legal defense. He came forward; but there was no more space given him than for one man to pass singly, for men were drawn up in formation on both sides, and Glúm was bidden to advance through that passage if he wished to go before the judicial court. That seemed to him inadvisable, and he said to his men: "It is evident that they believe they have control of matters; and maybe they have. However, I don't want you to turn back. I shall go first, then two abreast after me, then four abreast; and let us come at them with a rush, with our spears held before us. And then the wedge will advance if it is pressed hard."

They did so, and in one rush ran into the hallowed circle in which the judges sat in court, and it was a long time in the night before they were ousted; and there was such a great and hard thronging that only eventually were the judges able to convene again. And when they began to sum up the lawsuit Glúm went up on the hill of laws and adduced witnesses to testify that the sun was shining on the assembly field; whereupon by a lawful veto he forbade the judges to deliver a sentence; and then every case that had been brought up was to be dropped.

The meeting broke up then. The Esphœling people were much put out. Thórarin declared that Glúm had frustrated them shamefully. Einar said: "This does not seem so very bad to me as to you, because the suit can be taken up where it was dropped." Thereupon the Esphœling people, with Einar and many of their friends who had promised them assistance against Glúm, departed for the General Assembly (the Althing).[62] Glúm's kinsmen then supported him in his suit to a just decision. And, following the counsel of wise men, the case was adjudged in his favor if he would declare on his oath that he had not killed Thorvald Barb. And since many took an interest in the matter they agreed between them that Glúm should declare on his oath that he had not killed him. And it was also agreed on at what time this oath was to be sworn, which was in the fall, when five weeks of summer were left. The matter was followed up so energetically that it was decided that they would continue with the suit unless Glúm swore the oath in three sanctuaries of the Eyjafjörð District. Failure to take the oath was to be declared if he had not done so by that time. There was much speculation how Glúm's oath would be worded and spoken.

Chapter 25

Thereupon all went home from the Assembly. Glúm kept to his home during the summer, and peace prevailed in the district. Time passed till the Fall Assembly came around. From it, Glúm disappeared, so that no one knew where he was. Már stayed at home at the farm. But when five weeks of summer were left Már sent out invitations to a wedding, and no less than one hundred and twenty came. All thought there was something strange about this invitation, for those attending were folk of low degree. That evening one could see men riding in twos or fives from all the valleys around the Eyjafjörð. And when they all had arrived they gathered. Among them was Glúm, Ásgrím, and Gizur, at the head of three hundred and sixty men. They proceeded to Thverá and sat there during the night at the banquet.

On the following morning Glúm sent for Thórarin, requesting him to come to Djúpadal farm not later than at the sixth hour, there to listen to the oath. Thórarin responded and came with one hundred and twenty men. When they arrived at the sanctuary six men entered into

106

it: Gizur and Ásgrím with Glúm, and Einar and Hlenni the Old with Thórarin. He who was to swear the temple oath was to have a silver ring on his hand which had been reddened with the blood of an ox which had been slaughtered for sacrifice, and it was to weigh no less than three ounces. Then Glúm spoke as follows: "I call Ásgrím to witness, and I call Gizur to witness, that I swear the temple oath by the ring, and that I declare to the god that I was not there, and I killed not there, and I reddened not spear point or sword edge when Thorvald Barb was slain.[63] Consider now my oath, ye wise men who are present."

Thórarin and those with him were not prepared to find fault with the oath as such, but they did say that they never had heard it spoken that way. In a like manner oaths were sworn by Glúm at Gnúpafell farm and at Thverá. Both Gizur and Ásgrím remained several days at Thverá; and at their parting Glúm gave to Gizur the blue cloak, and to Ásgrím the spear inlaid with gold, and they parted as friends.

During the winter Thorvarð and Thórarin met, and Thorvarð asked: "Did Glúm swear the oath satisfactorily?" Thórarin answered: "We didn't find fault with it." Thorvarð said: "It is a strange thing that shrewd men can be so mistaken. I have known men to admit being responsible for manslaughter; but this I have never known or heard of, that they have taken an oath on themselves having committed manslaughter, as did Glúm. Else, how could he declare that more clearly than by saying that he did commit manslaughter there, and had been there, and had reddened spear point and sword edge where Thorvard Barb fell on the Hrísateig Field, even though he did not pronounce it the same way most people do. And this disgraceful trick on you is likely to be remembered for ever." Thórarin replied: "I did not notice that. And indeed, I am weary of having to fight with Glúm." Thorvarð replied: "If you feel too tired to fight Glúm on account of ill health, why not let Einar take up the suit again? He is shrewd and of noble birth, and many will support him. And Guðmund the Powerful, his brother, will not stand by and do nothing. In fact, that is what he (Einar) is most eager for—possession of Thverá farm."

Thereupon Einar and Thórarin met and consulted together. Thórarin said: "If you will conduct the case, many are likely to support you; and we shall manage to buy the land of Thverá for you at no greater cost than for what Glúm bought it from Thorkel the Tall." Einar answered: "Glúm has now disposed of the gifts, the fur cloak and the spear, which his father-in-law Vigfús made him and told him to hold on to, if he wanted to retain his position of influence, which he said he would lose if he gave them away. Now I shall take up the suit and press it."

Chapter 26

Thereupon Einar prepared the suit for manslaughter to be brought up at the General Assembly, and both sides collected large numbers of men. But before Glúm left his home he dreamed that many had come to Thverá to meet Frey, and it seemed to him as though he saw many assembled on the gravel banks by the river where Frey was sitting on his throne. He dreamed that he asked who had gathered there, and that he was given the answer: "They are your departed kinsmen, and we are praying Frey that you be not driven from Thverá farm. But it is of no avail, Frey answers shortly and wrathfully, and recalls the gift of an ox which Thorkel the Tall made him." He awoke then, but from that time on his relations with Frey would be worse, he said.

The time for the session of the General Assembly approached, and at the conclusion of the case against him Glúm admitted that it was he who had slain Thorvald. But at this point his friends and kinsmen interceded, so that terms were agreed on instead of his being declared outlaw or having to leave the country. These terms they agreed on: that Glúm paid half the price of the

Thverá estate to Ketil, the son of Thorvald Barb, as compensation for the slaying of his father, and sold half of it at the proper value. Nevertheless, he was to remain on his estate that year, thereafter to be banished from the district and to dwell no closer to it than in Horgárdal. Thereupon the Assembly broke up. Later, Einar bought the land, as had been agreed upon.

Einar's men went to Thverá in the spring in order to cultivate the ground. And Einar enjoined them to report to him every word Glúm spoke to them. One day Glúm talked with them and said: "It is evident that Einar has procured good workers, for the land is well tilled. Now it is important that care be bestowed on everything, both big and small. Here by the creek you are to erect a pole for the washing to be hung on. That is convenient for the women when they have large pieces to wash, for the home wells are poor."

The workmen returned to Einar's farm, and he asked them what they had talked about with Glúm. They reported how attentive he was to everything that was done. Einar said: "Did it appear to you that he wanted to get everything in shape for me?" They said: "So it seemed to us." Einar said: "It looks different to me. I am thinking that on that pole he means to hang you, and to put up a 'pole of insult'[64] for me. However, you are not to go there again."

In the spring Einar moved his residence to Thverá, while Glúm lingered to the very last day for moving. When his household were ready to leave Glúm seated himself in the highseat and did not start to leave though people called to him. He had his hall hung with tapestries, intending not to part with his lands like a poor cotter.—Hallbera, daughter of Thorodd Hjálmsson, was the mother of Guðmund and Einar. She resided at Hanakamb then. She came to Thverá, greeted Glúm, and said: "All hail, Glúm; but now you can stay here no longer. I have borne fire around Thverá land.[65] I turn you out with all that is yours, the land is now consecrated to the use of my son Einar." Thereupon Glúm arose and told her to stop jabbering, wretched woman that she was. Nevertheless, he then rode away. Looking back over his shoulder toward the farm he spoke this verse:

> 8. Like kings of old I cleared with
>   crew of men this farm land—
>   fame I gained by fighting—;
>   fain would I, woman, stay here.
>   But now, at length, lost I
>   the lands so broad and wide-flung
>   out of my hands for ever,
>   axe-wielder, in battle.

Glúm lived at Möðruvellir in the Horgárdal with Thorgrím Fjúk, but did not like it there longer than one year. After that he lived for two years in Myrkárdal. Then an avalanche descended near the farm, tearing away some of the buildings. Then Glúm spoke this verse:

> 9. Gladness never again the
>   giver-of-rings[66] will have now—
>   baleful woe from one blow did
>   banefully dash my spirits—.[67]
>   When here, high I bore my
>   head—less my living now is—
>   feeder-of-wolves-on-the-fallen,[68]
>   forty happy winters.

Then Glúm bought land at Thverábrekka in the Öxnadal and lived there the rest of his life, becoming blind in his old age.

Chapter 27

A certain man called Narfi lived on the island of Hrísey. Ulfeið had been his wife, the daughter of Ingjald, the son of Helgi the Lean. Their sons were Eyjólf, Klæng, Thorbrand, and Thorvald. They all were very capable men and akin to Glúm. Klæng and Eyjólf managed the farm on Hrísey Island after their father. A man called Thorvald lived at Hagi. He was nicknamed Menni and was married to Helga, a daughter of Thórð Hrafnsson of Stokkahlaða.

One spring Thorvald of Hagi came to Hrísey on a cargo boat, intending to go fishing, and when Klæng learned that he joined him. Now when they sailed out of the fjord they found a whale that had just died. They fastened ropes to it and during the day sailed with it in tow into the fjord. Klæng wanted to bring it to Hrísey, for that was a shorter distance than to Hagi, whereas Thorvald wanted it brought to Hagi, saying that he had the same legal rights and that it was against the law not to tow it to the place where the transporters owned land. Thorvald claimed the right to be on his side and declared that

112

Glúm's kinsmen need not encroach on his rights; "and whatever the law may be, the stronger are going to decide in this case." Thorvald had more men with him that time, and so they took the stranded whale from Klæng by force. Both of them owned land by the shore. Klæng returned home, much incensed. Thorvald and his men laughed at Klæng and his men, saying they did not dare to hold on to what was theirs.

One morning Klæng rose early, and with three others rowed to Hagi. He arrived there early and found people in the farm still asleep. Klæng said: "Now we shall devise a plan. Here are cattle by the fence, let's drive them up on the roof[69] under which Thorvald sleeps and thus entice him to come out." They did so, and Thorvald awoke and rushed out. Klæng made for him and inflicted a mortal wound on him, then left immediately as he did not dare to make known there the manslaughter he had committed, for a great many people were at hand, but rowed out seaward to his island, and there made public the manslaughter committed.

Now the duty of prosecuting devolved on Thórarin and Thórð. They called Klæng's deed murder.[70] During the time when this suit was brought before the Assembly Glúm remained at home. But while the Assembly was in session he betook himself to Svarfarðardal and to the Fljót District and sought support against the verdict of the court of execution; but he requested secrecy about his plan. Klaufi, who dwelled at Bárð's farm—he was the husband of Halldóra, the daughter of Arnór Redcheek—said: "We shall certainly give Glúm our support," and many others also promised him their assistance. Thereupon Glúm returned home.

The verdict of guilty was delivered at the Assembly, and thereupon they (Einar's party) made ready to execute the verdict.[71] They had four ships, with thirty men on board of each, and Einar, Thórarin and Thórð in command. Rowing from the inner reaches of the fjord they arrived at the island at dawn. They saw smoke above the houses. Einar asked his men whether it seemed to them, as it seemed to him, that the smoke[72] was not quite black. They replied that it seemed so to them too. Einar said: "From the appearance of the smoke it seems to me that a great number of men is in the houses and that it is the steam rising from humans. If that is the case we shall make a test and row away from the island in plain view and thus make certain if there are a great number of people on the island."

And so they did. But when the people on the island saw that, they rushed out and down to their boats and pursued them. It was Glúm who had come there with two hundred and forty men, and they chased them all the way to Oddeyr farm, and nothing came of the court of execution. So the Eyfirðing people earned nothing but humiliation from their expedition.

Glúm remained all summer at his farm. He was to consecrate the fall assembly. Its location is on the east side of the fjord, a short distance from Kaupang, and the people of the district gathered in great numbers, whereas Glúm had only thirty men. Many warned him that he should not attend the Assembly with only a few men. He replied: "Most likely the best part of my life is behind me; but I rejoice that they have not ever crowded me so that I could not pursue my even course."

Glúm sailed with his ship into the inner reaches of the fjord, landed, and proceeded toward the booths. Now there are steep banks of loose gravel between the shore of the fjord and the booths, and when Glúm and his men arrived opposite the booth owned by Einar, men rushed out of the booths, attacking them, and shoving them down from the gravel banks. Glúm fell and rolled himself down to the shore, protecting himself with his shield, and so suffered no wounds, but three spears stuck in his shield. Thorvald Tasaldi had just made the shore and saw that it looked bad for Glúm, so he jumped ashore, seized an oar, ran up the gravel bank, and hurled the oar at Guðmund the Powerful. It struck his shield, which broke, one piece of the oar hitting him on the chest with such force that he dropped unconscious and had to be carried to his booth in a sheet. Thereupon both sides spurred on their men, shooting and pelting each other with stones. It was a hard fight, and many were wounded, but all said with one accord that few men could have defended themselves more valiantly than Glúm and his band. Einar and his followers pushed the attack with vigor. Then men interceded between them. The outcome was that two of Glúm's band had fallen, Klæng Narfason and Grím Eyrarlegg, the brother of Glúm's wife Halldóra. At that time Brúsi Hallason spoke this verse:

> 10. Even, Óðin's maiden,[73]
> out we came in the fray 'gainst
> the sturdy steerers-of-sea-
> stags[74]—I know that for certain—.
> Yet did the chosen champions
> charge down the shingly hillocks,
> famous flinger-of-spearshafts,
> faster than we expected.

Einar spoke a verse:

> 11. The stalwart helmsman had to
> hie him down the shelving
> hummock—it was hard to

hinder—at the thingmeet,
the time his feet did find no
foothold, breaker-of-armrings,
(till he reached Ræfil's-
realm's wind-blown sand-dunes.)[75]

Then Glúm spoke a verse in reply:

12. The helmet-bearing host was
hesitant to come down the
brink where, buckler-shielded,
battle-eager, we stood, all
ready to feed the ravens.
Rash it seemed to the warriors,
steerer-of-ships, to start the
storm-of-missiles bloody.[76]

The suit was to be settled in this fashion that the death of
Klæng and that of Thorvald of Hagi should be set off
against each other. Also, the slaying of Grím Eyrarlegg
and the wounds inflicted on Guðmund were to be counted
as equal. Glúm was much put out by this conclusion of
the lawsuit, as he expressed in the verse he composed
later:

13. Ill it has grown on earth, and
old age plagues the poet.
Most of my life was passed midst the
murderous storm-of-Heðin,[77]
since in slaughterous contest,
sea-farer, they will not
let me, as I vowed, take
vengeance for Grím, my kinsman.

Chapter 28

One summer, when the brothers Guðmund the Powerful and Einar were riding home on their way from the
Assembly, Glúm invited people to come to his place.
He sent messengers up to Öxnadal Moor to invite the two
brothers to his home to tell them that now he wanted
to be fully reconciled with them, "because now, on account of my advanced age, I am capable of nothing,
and I shall invite them not only for a meal." Glúm had
at that time lost his eyesight. He had a watch kept on
their movements.

Guðmund was inclined to accept the invitation, but
Einar did not want to, each riding on his side of the river.
Glúm was told that only one group of men was riding
up to his place. Then he said: "In that case Einar most
likely will not accept my invitation. He is so suspicious
that he trusts no one."

We are told that Einar called out to Guðmund: "I am
likely to go there tomorrow if you go there this evening."
Guðmund reflected on what he said, and replied: "What
you probably mean is that you will have to take up the

prosecution when I am killed"; whereupon he turned and followed Einar. This was told Glúm and that neither of the two turned that way [i.e. to his farm]. "Too bad," said Glúm; "because it was my intention that if I encountered them I would not miss both." He had a short sword concealed under his cloak.

That was the end of the dealings between Glúm and the Eyfirðing clan. When Christianity came to this country[78] Glúm had himself baptized, and lived three more years after that. He was confirmed by Bishop Kol in his last illness and died in his white baptismal robe. At that time Már Glúmsson dwelled at Fornhagi and had a church built there. Glúm was buried there, as was Már when he died, together with many others, because for a long time there was no other church in Horgárdal. It is said that Glúm was for twenty years the greatest chieftain in the Eyjafjörð District, but that for another twenty years no one was more than his equal; also, that he was one of the doughtiest fighters in this land. And here ends the saga about Glúm.

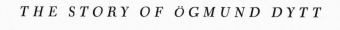

THE STORY OF ÖGMUND DYTT

Introduction

Two stories have been skillfully combined in the *þáttr*
which goes under the name of Ögmund Dytt. That of
Ögmund's delayed revenge may very well reflect a real
occurrence during the long rule of Earl Hákon Sigurðarson and the brief but glorious reign of his successor, the
missionary King Óláf Tryggvason of Norway; whereas
that of Gunnar Helming bears all the earmarks of a
Christian version of a well-attested heathen cultic rite
dressed up as a legendary tale appropriate among the
fairly numerous accounts of that nature associated with
the missionary activities of the two Óláfs—one for once
told with a sly bit of humor. Actually, of course, Gunnar
Helming is innocent of any wrong-doing. It is a case of
mistaken identity which puts him to flight, although, on
the other hand, his impersonation of a heathen divinity
lays him open to the suspicion of apostasy, so the clemency
of the king is not uncalled for.

This account of a man overcoming, then impersonating,
the fertility god Frey, and marrying his spouse, was for-
merly cited by mythologists as additional testimony of

the widely spread spring fertility rites in Northern Europe, for which there exists ample evidence. But a more careful scrutiny of it should have revealed the pervading *interpretatio Christiana* and hence its secondary value.

To be sure, a certain resemblance was seen to the oldest account of Frey worship in the ancient North, the famous 40th chapter of Tacitus's *Germania*, where we learn that seven tribes living on the coastal lands of the North Sea (or the Baltic) venerate the goddess Nerthus[1] in a sanctuary located in a forest on an island; that in it is a cart which only her high priest may touch; that when he is aware of her presence in the sanctuary she enters it and proceeds solemnly about the countryside while there is general rejoicing, and that on her return the cart, its fittings, and she herself are washed in a secret tarn and the slaves attending her are drowned in it.

As will be observed there are some similarities between our story and Tacitus's account, but even more divergencies. Moreover, since his writings were practically unknown in the Middle Ages we must assume that the author of our *þáttr* had gathered certain elements of his story from other sources unknown to us, possibly tales brought back by widely traveled compatriots from Uppsala where the Frey cult is known to have flourished till the times of Saxo Grammaticus (second half of the twelfth century): which tales he embellished with details in the clerical taste, such as Gunnar's inward prayer to help him overcome "the fiend," and his refusal to accept the sacrifice of animals.

An acquaintance with *Víga-Glúm's Saga* is evident. Glúm had also been a worshiper of Frey (before his last-minute conversion), and a stern upholder of the *lex talionis*, the moral necessity of maintaining the honor, not only of the offended individual, but of his kin, by aveng-

ing himself on the perpetrator of an insult. Though Ögmund is his fosterson he won't have anything to do with
him until he lives up to that principle. Once he has
done so Glúm is ready to take him back in his good graces.

L. M. H.

The Story of Ögmund Dytt

Ögmundar þáttr Dytts

At that time[2] there were in Iceland many respected men who could claim kinship with King Óláf Tryggvason. One of them was Víga-Glúm, the son of Eyjólf hrúga (Hulk) and Ástríð, the daughter of Hersir Vígfús, as was told before. Víga-Glúm's sister was named Helga. She was married to Steingrím of Sigluvík. Their son's name was Thorvald, nicknamed Tasaldi.[3]

A man had grown up with Víga-Glúm as his fosterson whose name was Ögmund, the son of Hrafn. Hrafn was a wealthy man who lived north by the Skagafjörð. He had been a thrall of Glúm and of Ástríð, Glúm's mother, and Glúm had freed him. Ögmund's mother was of the kin of the Guðdalers. We are not told her name, but she was related to Víga-Glúm. Ögmund was a handsome man, tall and accomplished, and in high favor with his kinsman Glúm. Glúm himself was advanced in years at the time and lived at Thverbrekka in Öxnadal when his kinsman Ögmund was full grown and when Vigfús, the son of Glúm, was in exile and in the retinue of Earl Hákon.

One summer Ögmund said to Glúm that he was eager to go abroad. "I would purchase me a ship at Gásar," he said, "and pay for it with my father's money, which is ample for that, but I would like to have help and approval for this venture." Glúm answered: "Many go abroad who are not more promising than you. Now it would seem more important to me that in your journey you acquire honor and renown, rather than much money, if there isn't the chance to acquire both."

Glúm bought him a ship from some Norwegians, and Ögmund got ready for his journey, stowing his ship with valuable goods that his father furnished him. Ögmund was to be captain of crew and ship. On it were few others than Icelanders who had never been abroad before. They put to sea rather late in the summer, with a favorable breeze. They continued with strong, yet favorable winds, and toward the end of their journey they sighted land in the evening. There was a fresh onshore breeze. Then the Norwegians who were the navigators said it would be safer to lower the sail and let the ship drift before the wind during the night and make land the next day in broad daylight. Ögmund answered them: "Let us not fail to make use of such a favorable breeze. Who knows whether it will continue tomorrow. Besides, there is bright moonlight tonight."

They did as they were told, and sailed on. When they were but a short distance from land they encountered in some strait many warships bound together by hawsers, but did not sight them before they ran down one of them, but continued on their course to harbor on the mainland.

Then some men who had been on the ship before remarked that they had proceeded foolishly. But Ögmund retorted that every one had to look out for himself.

Now these warships were commanded by Earl Hákon.

The one they had sunk belonged to a man called Hallvarð, a man of high rank and a great friend of the earl. All the goods on that ship were lost, but the crew was rescued.

Early next morning the earl was informed of the damage done and the disgrace inflicted on them. He flew into a rage at this news and said: "These men must be fools who haven't ever been to foreign parts. Now I give you, Hallvarð, permission to punish them and thus avenge your humiliation. They will hardly have a superior force to fight against, and you lack neither the courage nor the hardihood to inflict on them a similar or greater retribution, whoever they may be." Then Vigfús Viga-Glúmsson said: "You will no doubt be willing, sire, to accept compensation from them and spare their lives if they are ready to submit their case to your judgment. Let me go and find out what people they are and try to arrange a settlement, if possible." The earl replied: "You may do so; but I am thinking they will consider me mighty harsh in my imposition of payment for such a gross offence."

Vigfús rowed up to the merchantman and on it recognized his kinsman Ögmund and was glad to see him and asked for tidings from Iceland and about his father; and Ögmund told him what he asked about. Then Vigfús said: "Your case looks very bad, owing to this occurrence," and he explained then how matters stood, and also that Earl Hákon had only reluctantly consented to a settlement with the merchants. "Now it is my buiness with you, kinsman, to ask you to submit to the earl's decision. I shall plead your case as best I can, and matters may in some way turn out well." Ögmund answered: "From all I have heard about this earl I don't care to leave my case altogether to his decision, and especially so if he threatens harsh measures, because he is likely to carry out his threats. But I won't refuse if he talks in a conciliatory fashion." Vigfús replied: "It would be wise for you to consider what is best for you, because you have to deal with a man whose wrath you cannot bear up against if you refuse his decision."

Vigfús rowed back to the earl's ship and informed him that the men on the merchant ship were his fosterbrothers, and some of them, kinsmen. "And they are willing to submit their case to your decision." Then one of the earl's men spoke up: "That is not true, Vigfús, what you tell your lord. They offer you no acceptable compensation for what they have done." Then Hallvarð said: "Then it behooves me to exact revenge, and not to require other people's help."

The earl said he should do that. Vigfús said: "If I have my way I shall kill him who slays my kinsman Ögmund." Hallvarð replied: "Though you Icelanders are men of great mettle, yet I expect that people in this land, at least those who respect themselves, will not tolerate indignities without redress, whether from you kinsmen of Víga-Glúm or from others."

Thereupon Hallvarð rowed up to the merchantman, while the earl had Vigfús strongly guarded. Hallvarð approached the merchant ship and asked who was in command of it. Ögmund gave his name. Then Hallvarð said: "I and my companions make great charges against you, and we have come here to find out if you are willing to make fitting amends." Ögmund replied: "I shall not refuse to make amends if your demands are not too harsh." Hallvarð said: "You have to deal with men who will not accept trifles for heinous offences." Ögmund replied: "We shall refuse to make any amends if they are called for in such an overbearing manner." "And I," said

127

Hallvarð, "consider it most fitting and proper, not to ask you for what you may offer." And with that he leapt up on the merchant ship and struck Ögmund a blow with the hammer of his battle axe so that he fell at once unconscious.

Thereupon Hallvarð returned to the earl and told him what had happened. The earl said that much less had been done than was deserved. Hallvarð replied: "Their leader was the one most to be blamed in this matter, but I thought it wiser not to do more about it for the time being than to knock him unconscious. It was only proper that foul play was matched by foul play; but I reserve the right to take more revenge on him later if that is needed."

But when Vigfús learned what had happened he was highly incensed and would have liked to attack Hallvarð and kill him if he got the chance. But the earl had him guarded so he had no opportunity to do so.

Ögmund regained his senses, but he had a bad wound from the blow and lay long abed during the winter, but finally recovered. He was chaffed a great deal about this occurrence, so that wherever he went he was called Ögmund Dytt ("Blow"). But he acted as though he didn't know what people talked about.

Vigfús often came to see him and prompted him to avenge himself. "To achieve that," he said, "I shall lend you my assistance, so that you can avenge your indignities." Ögmund answered: "That is not my intention, kinsman. It would seem to me that in this affair I am not shamed any more than Hallvarð. And it was hardly to be expected that matters would come to a less serious termination, considering how violently we proceeded in the first place. It would be ill-advised to avenge Hallvarð's deed, seeing how close a friend he is with Earl Hákon in whose power you are here. Moreover I don't wish to repay your father Glúm by having you undergo the risk of certain loss of limb or life at my instigation." Vigfús replied: "I shall not thank you for that, nor will my father, that you act as though you were to look out for my safety, if I would not do that myself. I suspect you are swayed by cowardice rather than by caution, and it is an ill thing to help a man who has a hare's heart in his breast. More likely, too, that you take after your father's thrall kin mother than after the men of Thverá." They parted, with Vigfús in a towering rage.

Winter and spring passed. Then Ögmund got his ship ready and sailed to Iceland in summer, after acquiring much property on his journey. He landed in the Eyjafjörð, and Glúm soon heard of his arrival. He also was told right away what insult Ögmund had suffered. As soon as Ögmund had made provision for his ship and wares he rode to the Thverá farm and stayed with Glúm for a while.

Glúm was very cool to Ögmund, in fact rather resented his coming there. Ögmund on his part behaved most cheerfully and put on great airs. He went to all meetings in the neighborhood, indeed, proved rather meddlesome in people's affairs. And whenever a disagreement arose between men no one was more enterprising and quick in trying to settle matters between them. Also, he was active in all that needed to be done on Glúm's farm or in bringing up supplies, and acted most self-important. But for a long time Glúm would not speak with him.

One day Glúm said to him: "I want you to know, Ögmund, that I feel no obligation to you for your work. Also, it seems strange to me that you are so eager to meddle in other people's affairs, seeing that you show no energy in your own. Your first journey abroad turned

129

out so wretchedly that I would rather not see you any more since you choose to be a shame to yourself and a reproach to all your kinsmen and to be forever called a coward, not daring to avenge yourself."

Ögmund replied: "However, consider this, kinsman, what reason I had for refraining from revenge: I thought it mighty risky to attempt revenge on account of your son Vigfús." "You did not need to have considered that," said Glúm, "since he did not consider that himself. I would have been prepared to have you both slain if you had shown the courage to avenge yourself. Now one of two things is true: either you are so exceedingly steadfast, and more long-suffering than others, in that you can afford to wait to show your manhood, even though belatedly—in which case you would not have proved yourself such a coward; or else you are altogether worthless and that trait shows itself to be stronger in you which is worse befitting your station and, as the saying goes: 'oft falls short in bravery the unfree race of thralls.' However that may be, I don't want you to be about me any longer."

Thereupon Ögmund went to stay with his father. But when he had spent two years in Iceland he got his ship ready during the summer, collected a crew, and sailed to Norway. He made his landfall in the north, near Throndheim, and proceeded into the fjord. Late in the day he moored his ship near Niðarholm. Next day Ögmund said: "Now we shall launch the boat, and I shall row up the river to find out what news there are on land."

He put on a two-colored cloak bordered with laces about the shoulder seam, a valuable garment, and entered the boat with two other men. That was early in the morning. They rowed up to the landing stages. Just then they saw a man walk down to the river. He was in a hooded mantle made of scarlet cloth, all embroidered with figures.

He came down to the landing stage and asked who was in charge of the boat. Ögmund gave him his name. The townsman asked: "Are you Ögmund Dytt?" "Some men call me so," he replied. "And what is your name?" The man answered: "My name is Gunnar Helming [Half-and-Half]. And I am so called because I enjoy wearing garments of two colors." Ögmund inquired what news there was in the land. Gunnar answered: "The biggest piece of news is that Earl Hákon is dead, and a noble king has come to succeed him, Óláf Tryggvason." Ögmund inquired further: "Do you know where a man called Hallvarð lives, a citizen of Throndheim of noble stock and wealthy?" Gunnar answered: "No wonder you ask after him. He is now called Hallvarð Háls [Wryneck], because he took part in the Battle of the Jómsvíkings[4] last winter, under Earl Hákon, and there received a deep gash in his neck behind the ear, so that since that time he carries his head tilted sideways. He lives in town here with King Óláf's bodyguard and has been highly honored by him. But you, Ögmund, have a fine cloak there, beautifully dyed in two colors. Would you sell me your cloak?" Ögmund said: "No, I will not sell it, but if you like it so much I will give it to you." "Let me have it, and a blessing on you," said Gunnar. "And I shall repay you for this gift, but for the first, take this mantle in return. Who knows but it may stand you in good stead."

With that, Gunnar returned a little ways into the town, wearing the cloak, while Ögmund slipped into his mantle. He said to his companions: "Now I want you to fasten the boat loosely to the bank by the stern, just enough so it won't drift from the shore, while I go up into the town. And you are to sit on your benches with your oars handy."

Thereupon Ögmund went up into the town, meeting but few people. In one house a door stood open where some men were washing their hands. One of them was very tall and of handsome appearance who carried his head tilted. From what Gunnar had told him Ögmund inferred that this might be Hallvarð. Ögmund went up to the door, and everybody in the room thought they recognized Gunnar Helming. Ögmund in a low voice requested Hallvarð to come out to him on account of a little matter, "For I have a pressing and swift business to transact with you," he said. He then stepped aside from the door, drawing the sword he carried. Gunnar Helming was on speaking terms with everybody, and so Hallvarð went out alone. As soon as they met Ögmund dealt him his death blow. Then he ran down to the boat, cast off the mantle, put a stone in the hood, and threw it out into the river where it sank down to the bottom. Ögmund entered the boat and bade his men row out of the river. And when they reached the merchantman he called out to his men: "There is much strife here on land, a hard wind is blowing out of the fjord seaward; so let's hoist sail and make our way back to Iceland."

His men said he acted as though he was afraid, if he did not dare to go on land even if people there fought with one another. They did, however, as he commanded and sailed back to Iceland, landing in the Eyjafjörð.

Ögmund went to see Víga-Glúm and told him about his journey, and said that his revenge had been accomplished, even though long delayed. Glúm then was greatly pleased and said he had anticipated that he would become a doughty man eventually. Ögmund then stayed with Glúm during the winter as a highly honored guest.

But now we must revert to Hallvarð's followers. As they thought he took too long to come back inside they went out and found him lying dead in his blood. King Óláf was told the news, and also that it was thought that Gunnar Helming had slain him. The king remarked: "I would not have suspected him to have committed that deed; yet he is to be hunted down and hanged, if indeed he is guilty."

Gunnar Helming had a brother called Sigurð, a wealthy man and one of King Óláf's bodyguard, and very dear to the king. He was in the town at that time, and as soon as he became aware that his brother's life was in danger he went in search for him and located him. And Sigurð asked Gunnar whether he was guilty of the deed attributed to him. Gunnar declared that there was no truth to that. Sigurð said: "Yet it is believed that it was true. Tell me what you know about this affair." Gunnar answered: "That I will not tell you nor any one else for the present." Sigurð said: "Then save your life."

Gunnar did so. He took to the woods and was not found. Afterwards he made his way east over the mountains and across Uppland,[5] everywhere in disguise, nor paused before issuing out of the woods in Sweden. Great sacrifices were being made at that time for Frey. He had been worshiped there for a long time, and his image was so greatly strengthened by magic spells that the devil spoke to people out of it. Frey was given a young and handsome woman to serve him; for it was the belief of the natives that he was a living being—as seemed to be the case in certain respects, and they thought he needed cohabitation with his wife. She was to have charge of the sanctuary, together with Frey, and of everything belonging to it.

Gunnar Helming issued from the woods at that spot and begged Frey's spouse to help him and be allowed to stay there with them. She looked him over and asked who he was. He replied that he was a wayfarer of low degree and a foreigner. "You don't seem to be a lucky man in all respects," she said, "for Frey is eyeing you in a hostile fashion. But rest yourself here for three nights, and then we shall see whether Frey will be better pleased with your looks." Gunnar replied: "It would seem better to me to have your help and protection than Frey's."

Gunnar was a cheerful and most entertaining person. Now when three nights had passed he asked Frey's spouse what the chances were for his staying there. "I don't know for certain," she said. "You are a poor devil, yet maybe you are of a good family, and I would be rather inclined to lend you help. However, Frey does not like you, and I fear his wrath is kindled. Stay here for another month, and let us see then what will happen." Gunnar said: "It turns out just as I would like it, that Frey hates me while you help me, because I consider him an evil fiend."

Gunnar pleased people the more the longer he stayed there, because of his entertaining ways and his manly bearing. He spoke again to Frey's wife, asking about his prospects. She answered: "People like you, and it seems to me a good idea that you remain here and then accompany Frey and me to banquets when there is sacrifice made to him for a good reason. Yet he hates you." Gunnar thanked her for her kind words.

Time passed now till they departed from their home. Frey and his wife were to sit in the cart, and their servant men were to go in front of it. They had a long way to go over a certain mountain road. Then they were caught in a violent snowstorm, and the roads became hard to travel. Gunnar was expected to go along with the cart and lead the horses. But after a while the servant men drifted away, leaving Gunnar alone behind beside Frey and his consort in the cart. Then Gunnar became very tired leading the draft horses, and after a while gave up walking ahead and seated himself in the cart, letting the horses find their way. Before long Frey's wife said to Gunnar: "Go on and lead the horses, or else Frey will set upon you."

He did so for a while, but when he became worn out again he said: "I shall risk now to stand up against Frey if he attacks me." Then Frey got out of the cart, and they began to wrestle with one another, and Gunnar began to give ground. He saw this wouldn't do, so he bethought that if he managed to overcome this fiend and it was granted to him to return to Norway, that he would return to the true faith and make his peace with King Óláf if he would take him back in grace. And straightway when he had thus bethought himself Frey began to totter. Thereupon he fell, and out of his image came the fiend that had been concealed in him, leaving behind an empty block of wood, one that Gunnar broke to pieces. Thereupon he gave the woman the choice, either that he would leave her and look out for himself, or else declare, when they came again to people, that he was Frey. She declared that she would rather do the latter.

Then he put on the idol's clothes. The weather began to clear, and after a while they arrived at the place where a sacrificial feast was planned for them. Many of the men who should have gone with them and helped them were there too. And now they thought it remarkable how Frey had shown his power in making his way to people with his wife in such weather when all had left them in the lurch, and also that now he was able to walk and associate with others and eat and drink like others.

During the winter the two attended other feasts prepared by the people. Frey always was chary of speech with others; and in the end he refused to have animals

135

slaughtered for him, as had been the custom before, and he would not accept any sacrifice, nor any gifts or offerings except gold and silver, good clothes, or other valuable things.

As time passed people thought that Frey's wife was with child. That seemed to them most excellent, and by the Swedes these signs were thought to be very promising in this their god; the weather turned mild, and everything looked so promising of a good season that no one remembered to have seen the like.

These news spread widely, how powerful this heathen god of the Swedes proved himself to be, and this came also to the ears of King Óláf Tryggvason, and he suspected what was at the bottom of this. And one day in spring he summoned Sigurð, Gunnar Helming's brother, to confer with him. The king asked him whether he had heard anything of Gunnar's whereabouts. Sigurð said he knew nothing. The king said: "I have an idea that this heathen god of the Swedes of whom we hear so much these days and whom they call Frey may actually be your brother Gunnar; because those sacrifices are said to be most potent when living humans are sacrificed. Now I shall send you to those parts in the east after him. Because it is abominable to learn that a Christian person's soul is to perish so miserably. I shall harbor no more wrath against him if he will of his own accord come before me, for I know now for certain that it was Ögmund Dytt who killed Hallvarð and not Gunnar."

Sigurð started at once on his journey to find this Frey, and he recognized his brother Gunnar. He delivered to him the message and the words of King Óláf. Gunnar answered: "I would be eager to go and make peace with King Óláf; but if the Swedes become aware how matters stand they are likely to kill me." Sigurð said: "We shall

136

secretly make our way from here and put our faith in what is most likely to be the case, which is that the luck and goodwill of King Óláf with God's mercy will be more powerful than the ill will and pursuit of the Swedes."

So Gunnar and his wife got themselves ready and had with them all the movable possessions they managed to take along, and they started out secretly at night.

But when the Swedes became aware of this they thought they knew the real cause and at once sent men in pursuit of them. But they had got but a short way when they lost their bearings and did not find the two; whereupon they gave up their pursuit and returned. But Sigurð, Gunnar, and his wife did not stop till they encountered King Óláf. He became reconciled with Gunnar and had his wife baptized, and they persisted thereafter in the true faith.

Notes and References

Introduction to Víga-Glúm's Saga

1. Actually, up to now there has been but one complete English translation, by Sir Edmund Head, 1866.

2. Literally "Calf of a Plank-built Barn." It was not uncommon for persons to bear animal names; thus *Úlfr* (Wolf), *Björn* (Bear), *Hrafn* (Raven), *Már* (Gull), etc.

3. See *Sturlunga saga*, Chapter 76.

4. For a brief account of the contents and technique of skaldic verse see the author's *The Skalds*. Princeton University Press, 1945. Reprinted by the University of Michigan Press, 1968.

Víga-Glúm's Saga

1. One of the best known settlers of Iceland, of princely origin. He took possession of the land about the Eyjafjörð.

2. The *goði* was both the priest and the temporal leader of a district. Originally there were 36 such in Iceland, but they were augmented later, with the growing numbers of settlers.

3. District in western Norway.

4. It was the custom, especially in later times, for young Icelanders of high birth to go abroad—mostly to Norway, where they had family connections, but also to Denmark and Sweden, there to complete their education by a sojourn at the residence of some nobleman or ruler.

5. †961. For the story how he became the fosterson of King Aethelstan of England, see Snorri's *Heimskringla*, The Saga of Harald Fairhair, Chapter 39.

139

6. Approximately of the social rank of a lord or baron.

7. Viz., to invite people to his banquet.

8. I.e., a wood bear, not the white, or polar, bear with which Icelanders were more familiar.

9. We agree with Turville-Petre's surmise that the *tólfmenningr* of the original text is a scribal error for *tvímenningr,* an arrangement according to which two, whether men or women, drank from the same horn.

10. It was commonly believed that the good fortune or luck of a superior person could be transferred to another.

11. As a second.

12. The reason for this (historic) personage having this nickname is not known. All the persons mentioned here figure in Icelandic and Norwegian history. We are to understand that Eyjólf married into a distinguished family.

13. Actually, like the neighboring Thverá, on the east bank of the river watering the Eyjafjörð Valley.

13a. Now Voss, in western Norway.

14. Female divinities.

15. In old Iceland fences were built of loose stones and turf.

16. Nanna is the god Baldr's wife; the whole, a kenning for "lady."

16a. Household.

17. Kenning for "battle."

18. Probably located across Thverá Creek from Glúm's farm. The name means "sure-giver."

19. If the General Assembly, the Althing, is meant, this was held in early summer, at Thingvellir, in southwestern Iceland.

20. The meaning of this proverbial saying is that pursuit and vengeance are most likely immediately after the deed. Glúm expects Thorkel and his kin to attack him at Hólar; but they let three nights elapse without doing so.

21. A warning that Thorkel might take vengeance on him (Thorstein) if he could not reach Glúm.

22. The play on words in Thorkel's reply cannot be rendered in the translation.

23. *Dís,* a female divinity; the whole, a kenning for "woman."

24. Frigg is the name of Óðin's wife; the whole, a kenning for "woman."

25. A valkyrie. The valkyries choose the heroes fallen on the battlefield and conduct them to Valhöll (Valhalla).

26. This seems to have been the practice when a dead person was summoned for a deed which made him outlaw.

27. After disinterring him.

140

28. I.e., he will see to it that Thorkel, as an outlaw, will be killed.

29. Such were used for weights on scales, and many have been found, at least in Norway.

30. I.e., the Althing, held in southwestern Iceland, where people from all parts of Iceland congregated in early summer for adjudicating quarrels and making new laws.

31. On the east side of the Skógafjörð. It has been argued that the Vöðlathing, held at the head of the Eyjafjörð, is meant, for that is where the spring court was held for the North Quarter.

32. This whole chapter is closely paralleled by Chapter 26 of the *Reykdœla saga ok Víga Skútu*. In Chapter 25 of that saga it is stated that Skúta sent Thorlaug back to Glúm to spite him.

33. It is actually directly east of Thverá.

34. I.e., of silver or gold.

35. Figuratively, outlaws. There are no wolves in Iceland. And the verse does not apply to the situation.

36. All like a shepherd.

37. *Skúti* means "cave."

38. The verdict of "the twelve" was that of a jury of eleven, appointed by the *goði* of the defendant's bailiwick, the twelfth being the *goði* himself.

39. Cf. the English "milk beard." Both allegations were regarded as grave insults, insinuating effeminacy.

40. Sizable timber had to be bought in Norway.

41. "Fated to die." The dead men are departed members of the family calling him to Hel (the Nether World).

42. Possibly, the present Mjaðmárdal.

43. This was regarded a reason for suspecting more intimate relations.

44. Here a circumlocution for the Espihól people.

45. Kenning for "sword."

46. Kenning for "mariner, warrior."

47. Unknown proverb.

48. Valkyries; the trough is filled with the flesh and blood of fallen warriors.

49. "Brushwood Field."

50. Kenning for "(generous) man."

51. Kenning for "blood."

52. One of Óðin's names. He is the strife-provoking god.

53. So nicknamed because both her father and her mother had children from previous marriages.

54. In serving the summons.

55. By attacking Glúm.

56. For seduction. —Though dead he could be summonsed; see Note 25.

57. Very likely close to Espihól. The following action is not quite clear.

58. Thund is one of Óðin's names: "Help from Óðin"(?). But probably the name is coined *ad hoc* by Glúm.

59. Supplied by the translator.

60. Kenning for "lady." The stanza is defective.

61. It was held in spring on the east coast of the Skagafjörð.

62. The General Assembly (Althing) was held in late spring. The location was in southwest Iceland, north of Lake Thingvallavatn. As the distance from the Eyjafjörð District is considerable and the journey over the central highlands difficult at all times, one would have expected the author to say more about this change of venue.

63. The equivocation in Glúm's oath lies in his using the preposition *at*, which monosyllabic word in the legal and poetic usage of Iceland had the force of a negative particle when suffixed to a verb: *Varek at þar*, "I was there," as against *varekat þar*, "I was not there."

64. The *niðstöng* was a pole, erected at a conspicuous point, with a magic curse in runic script scratched on it and/or a horse's skull topping it.

65. A rite of legal, rather than religious, significance.

66. Kenning for "generous man, chieftain," here Glúm.

67. The mortal blow he dealt Thorvald Barb, see Chapter 25.

68. Kenning for "warrior."

69. It was not uncommon for goats and sheep to graze on the turf covering the low roofs of houses.

70. Because the slaying of Thorvald was not made known to the nearest neighbor, as the law required.

71. It evidently was a verdict of outlawry, which called for a "Court of Execution." This consisted of eleven men named by the *goði* of the district, and himself. They confiscated the defendants' property, dividing it among creditors and/or prosecutors, with a certain portion going to the *goði* and the inhabitants of the district. In this case a great number of men were needed to overcome the anticipated resistance they would meet.

72. It was evidently a still, cold morning.

73. Kenning for "valkyrie, maiden, woman."

74. Sea-stag is a kenning for "ship."

75. Ræfil is the name of a sea-king; his realm is "the sea."

76. Kenning for "battle."

77. Heðin is a famous hero; the whole, a kenning for "battle."

78. It was adopted by the Althing in 1000 A.D.

1. Nerthus is equivalent, sound for sound, with Old Norse Njorðr, the father of Frey and Freya.

2. I.e., during the reign of Earl Hákon Sigurðarson (976-995).

3. Probably "overbearing man."

4. On this important event, see *Heimskringla*, "The Saga of Óláf Tryggvason," Chapters 34-43, and the *Jómsvíkinga Saga*.

5. However, the Norwegian province of Uppland (Oppland) lies far to the south of the route he probably took.